TARGET

TARGET

TARGET

Light A.A.

GERMAN COASTAL RADAR STATIONS
THEN AND NOW

When I was asked in 1941 what good it was my collecting detailed intelligence on all German radar stations, I replied we were going back and those stations might stand between our success and failure.

PROFESSOR R. V. JONES, 1978

GERMAN COASTAL RADAR STATIONS
THEN AND NOW

Winston Ramsey and Jean Paul Pallud

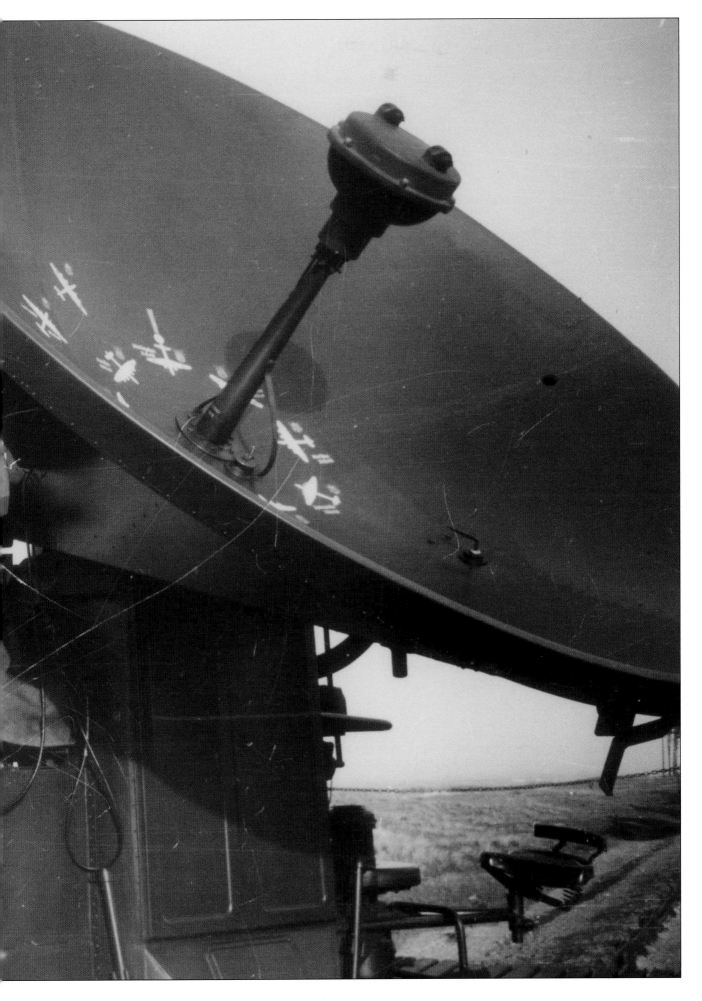

Credits

ISBN: 978 1870067 041
© *After the Battle* 2021

PUBLISHERS
Battle of Britain International Ltd
The Mews, Hobbs Cross House,
Hobbs Cross, Old Harlow,
Essex CM17 0NN

Telephone: 01279 41 8833.
Fax: 01279 41 9386
E-mail: hq@afterthebattle.com
Website: *www.afterthebattle.com*

PRINTERS
Printed by SRP Ltd, Exeter EX2 7LW, UK.

ACKNOWLEDGEMENTS
This book could not have been completed
without the help of Chris Ransted, Karel
Margry, Editor of *After the Battle*, and my
wife Gail. Thanks are also extended to Seb
Cox of the Air Historical Branch, Bernard
Paich and Peter Gunn.
Photographs are also included from the
After the Battle archive and from the collec-
tion of the Society for the Studies of the
European Theater of Operations.

Editorial Note

In June 2002, esteemed aviation historian and author Bruce Robertson contacted
me regarding an unpublished piece he had written on 'German Coastal Radars' as
he was hoping that we could include it in *After the Battle*. When the text arrived it
was accompanied by a huge packet of plans, aerial photographs and descriptions
covering over 60 radar stations sited by the Germans along the English Channel.
These files had been prepared in 1943-44 as target material for the forthcoming
invasion and straightaway I felt that it would be wasted if it was only used for a
story in the magazine. Instead it warranted being published as a book.

In sending me his material, Bruce was aware that he did not have long to live but
I promised him that we would publish his story although sadly publication has come
too late for Bruce to enjoy the finished product as he died in May 2004.

Bruce was the author of nearly a hundred books on aviation subjects including
the classic Harleyford series in the 1950s, so it is without question that the dedi-
cation of this book should be to his memory.

I have used Bruce's original article as our introduction, while the late Professor
R. V. Jones explains the rationale behind the creation of the actual intelligence
files. The text that follows is the actual description prepared for attacking each
individual target.

Finally, I am indebted to my co-author Jean Paul Pallud for spending countless
hours establishing the present-day locations of the radar sites, and marking them on
Google Earth cover, reproduced under licence.

However, to set the scene, I thought we should begin with an account of the
important operation which took place in February 1942 to land in France and bring
back parts from one of the radars for detailed examination in Britain. The site at
Bruneval was chosen, our text being based on *Instruments of Darkness* by
permission of the late Dr Alfred Price.

WINSTON RAMSEY, 2021

Contents

6   Introduction — BRUCE ROBERTSON
24   The Bruneval Raid — ALFRED PRICE
46   Operations Against Coastal Radar Stations — R. V. JONES
50   Ypres/Voormezele (Target No. 1)
52   Dunkirk/Fort des Dunes (Target No. 2)
57   Gravelines/Le Clipon (Target No. 3)
58   Gravelines/Petit-Fort-Philippe (Target No. 4)
60   Cap Blanc-Nez (Target No. 5)
65   Cap Blanc-Nez/St Pol (Target No. 6)
66   Cap Gris-Nez (Target No. 7)
68   Cap Gris-Nez/Pointe du Riden (Target No. 8)
70   Cap Gris-Nez/Bellevue (Target No. 9)
72   Cap Gris-Nez/Wattermel St George (Target No. 10)
74   Cap Gris-Nez/Onglevert (Target No. 11)
76   Boulogne/Boursin (Target No. 12)
78   Boulogne/Monument (Target No. 13)
79   Boulogne/Mont Lambert (Target No. 14)
80   Boulogne/Cap d'Alprech (Target No. 15A)
82   Boulogne/Cap d'Alprech (Target No. 15B)
83   Boulogne/Hardelot (Target No. 16)
84   Mont Violette (Target No. 17)
85   Neufchâtel/Mont St Frieux (Target No. 18)
86   Le Touquet/Plage Ste Cécile (Target No. 19)
88   Fruges/Prédefin (Target No. 20)
90   Aubigny/Frévillers (Target No. 21)
92   Berck-sur-Mer (Target No. 22)
94   Cayeux/Nouveau Brighton (Target No. 23)
96   Amiens/Montrelet (Target No. 24)
98   Abbeville/Vaudricourt (Target No. 25)
100   Le Tréport/Mont Huon (Target No. 26)
101   Dieppe/Caude-Côte (Target No. 27)
104   St Valéry-en-Caux/Manneville-ès-Plains (Target No. 28)
106   St Valéry-en-Caux/St Martin-aux-Buneaux (Target No. 29)
108   Fécamp/Chapelle de la Vierge (Target No. 30)
110   Cap d'Antifer/Sémaphore (Target No. 31)
112   Cap d'Antifer (Target No. 32)
116   Yvetot/Épinay-sur-Duclair (Target No. 33)
118   Neufchâtel/Sully (Target No. 34)
120   Le Havre/Cap de la Hève (Target No. 35)
122   Lisieux/Le Theil-Nolent (Target No. 36)
124   Bernay/La Chalière (Target No. 37)
126   Houlgate/Sémaphore (Target No. 38)
128   Caen/Douvres-la-Délivrande (Target No. 39)
134   Arromanches (Target No. 40)
135   Pointe et Raz de la Percée (Target No. 41)
138   St Lô/Bourg d'Enfer (Target No. 42)
139   Vire/Le Parc (Target No. 43)
140   Barfleur/Le Vicel (Target No. 44)
144   Cherbourg/Cap Lévy (Target No. 45)
146   Cherbourg/Fermanville (La Brasserie) (Target No. 46)
148   Omonville la Rogue/Asselins (Target No. 47)
150   Cap de la Hague/Auderville (Target No. 48)
154   Cap de la Hague/Jobourg (Target No. 49)
156   Cap de Carteret/Sémaphore (Target No. 50)
158   Guernsey/Fort George (Target No. 51)
160   Guernsey/Pleinemont (Target No. 52)
162   Jersey/Rouge Nez (Target No. 53)
163   St Malo/Pointe du Grouin (Target No. 54)
164   Cap Fréhel/Sémaphore (Target No. 55)
166   Moncontour/Bel-Air (Target No. 56)
168   Loudéac/La Récompense (Target No. 57)
170   Monterfil/Les Épinais (Target No. 58)
171   Vitré/La Haye (Target No. 59)
172   Oisseau/Marêtre (Target No. 60)
173   Falaise/Ri (Target No. 61)
174   Dieppe/Ste Marguerite (Target No. 62)
175   St Valéry-en-Caux/St Léger (Target No. 63)
176   Bayeux/Le Mesnil (Target No. 64)
178   Calais/Sangatte (Target No. 65)
182   Postscript
187   Index

Introduction

Danesfield House at Medmenham in Buckinghamshire became the main interpretation centre for photo-reconnaissance over Europe.

By Bruce Robertson

After the collapse of France in July 1940, German forces in the occupied territories manned the coasts of Holland, Belgium and France with Observer Posts. These posts had the dual purpose of preventing Allied personnel from escaping to England and also reporting any incursion from Britain by sea or air. The posts were manned by Wehrmacht personnel seconded to an Observer

After the First World War, aerial photography in Britain was primarily carried out by the Aircraft Operating Company (AOC) which took over Aerofilms Ltd in 1925. Amalgamated into H. Hemmings & Partners in 1933, with its head office at No. 5 Buckingham Place, SW1, its factory was at Wembley, close to the company's operating base at Heston. On May 31, 1940, the staff and equipment of AOC were taken over by the Air Ministry and renamed the Photographic Interpretation Unit. When the Wembley factory was damaged by bombing, the Ministry requisitioned Danesfield House which was then being used as a temporary home for boys evacuated from a prep school at Hammersmith. There, the RAF set up the Central Interpretation Unit (CIU) that became better known just as RAF Medmenham. Later that year it absorbed the Bomber Command Damage Assessment Section, followed by the Night Photographic Interpretation Section of No. 3 Photographic Reconnaissance Unit from Oakington in February 1942.

Corps organisation, the need for which had not been pre-planned.

By the end of 1941 the Germans had also established a chain of radar stations along the coast, manned by Wehrmacht signals personnel, grafted into the observer chain and so eliminating the need for some of the posts.

A weakness of German radar at first was an inability to identify friend from foe, lacking the facility of IFF that alerted friendly aircraft to the British defences. It was mid-war before German aircraft were fitted with FuGe25/25A equipment and their radars modified to recognise this facility. In the interim, lacking such information, it was necessary for the Luftwaffe to pre-declare flying movements to radio location station operators, leading on occasions to confusion.

Thirty-six million prints were produced at Medmenham during the war, being examined by a staff that eventually rose to over 1,700, of whom 150 were WAAFs.

In September 1940, Hermann Göring, created Reichsmarschall on July 19 following the defeat of France, travelled to the Channel coast to take charge of the attack planned on London. From September 6 to 8, his forward headquarters was established in The Hague (Netherlands), moving to Ronce (Belgium) from the 8th to the 15th, and Boulogne (France) from the 15th to 17th. On the day the new phase of the Battle of Britain commenced — Saturday, September 7 — the Reichmarschall's personal train 'Robinson' took him to the Pas-de-Calais where he proceeded with Luftwaffe commander Generalfeldmarschall Albert Kesselring and General der Flieger Bruno Lörzer, commanding II. Fliegerkorps, to Cap Gris-Nez to watch with his entourage as the formations set out for Britain.

The standard radars installed by the Germans on the most threatened coastline from Belgium down to Brittany were of three main types. Most common were the Freyas, the first standard German radar, with an aircraft detection range of some 125 miles. With modifications it remained the most common German radar throughout the war. They were delivered with a limber for road transport but along the coast they were mostly emplaced. Freyas consisted of a rotating steel cabin on which were mounted, one above the other, aerial frames approximately 20 feet by 8 feet, and when FuGe25/25A came into use a small third frame was added.

With Germany now having to defend a coastline of over 1,500 miles, the construction of 'the Atlantic Wall' began comprising fortifications and gun batteries. This was the inauguration of the Lindemann battery (named after the captain of the *Bismarck*) at Sangatte, just south of Calais. It comprised three casemates — this is Cäsar — mounting 406mm (16-inch) guns. The battery was protected by passive defences against insurgent aircraft provided by the chain of radar stations.

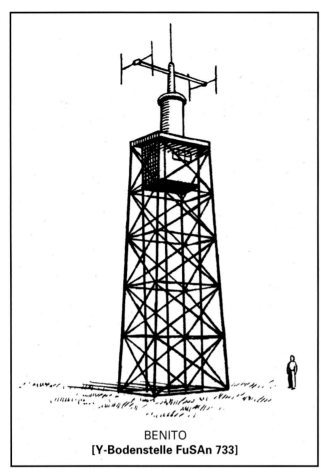

BENITO
[Y-Bodenstelle FuSAn 733]

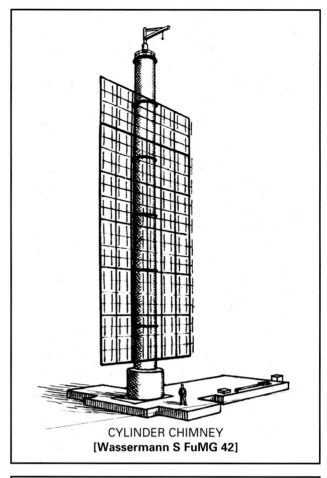

CYLINDER CHIMNEY
[Wassermann S FuMG 42]

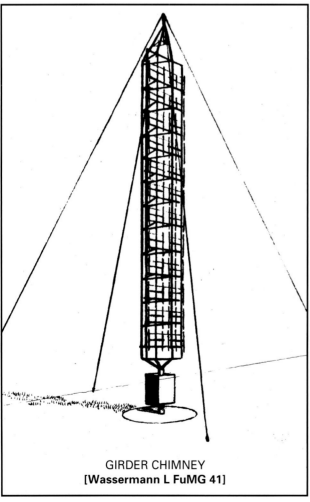

GIRDER CHIMNEY
[Wassermann L FuMG 41]

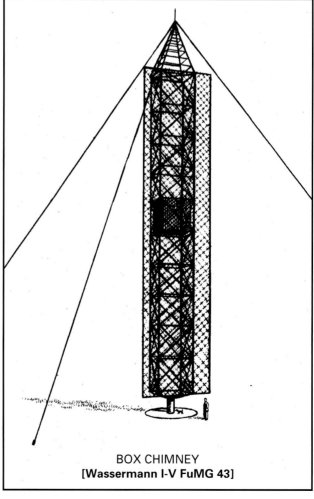

BOX CHIMNEY
[Wassermann I-V FuMG 43]

Left: The basic Freya had a range of around 125 miles — quite enough to police the English Channel and for stations in Holland to monitor Bomber Command formations assembling for a raid. In its basic form the receiver array was mounted above the transmitter array. Operating on the 2.5-metre wavelength with a power of 20 kilowatts, it was developed into several different guises as the basic aerial array could be stacked either vertically or horizontally. *Right:* The Wassermann (Cylinder Chimney) consisted of as many as eight Freya aerials mounted on a single column to give height and extend the coverage. *Below:* The Mamut (Mammoth), named Hoarding by the CIU, lived up to its name as the huge arrays measured from 20 to 30 metres wide and 14 to 16 metres high. It consisted of 192 dipoles giving 200 kilowatts that could be 'fired' in groups at a variety of horizontal angles up to 100 degrees from the beam. The Mammut had the equivalent of 16 ordinary Freyas giving a range of 200 miles.

The Würzburg, developed by the Gesellschaft für Elektro-akustische und Mechanische Apparate (GEMA) and Telefunken, was intended as a gun-laying radar. Working at 54-53 centimetres — a very short wavelength for that time — it had a range of 29 kilometres (18 miles) with an accuracy of plus or minus 25 metres (80 feet).

To the stations with Freyas, the small mobile Würzburg radars were added. The early types were mounted on a four-wheel trailer with a turntable but later models had limbers like Freyas. Their main feature was a 10-foot-diameter sheet metal paraboloid reflector that could be elevated. They had various functions such as measuring aircraft range, bearing and height, so supplementing Freyas, or for flak and searchlight control and sea watch. Along the French coast they were often emplaced with a small cabin built around the gear and an operator's seat behind the reflector.

As RAF Bomber Command increased its attacks on targets in the occupied countries and the German homeland, coastal and inland aircraft control and reporting stations and fighter control interception stations were opened up. Wary of probing raids from the sea and bombardment by Allied navies, aircraft reporting stations were interspersed with coast watching stations manned by German Navy personnel, usually established at former French Navy semaphore stations. The Navy used a special Coast-watcher radar, in general resembling Freyas but with a wire-mesh frame carrying two rows of vertical dipole aerials.

Later these stations were supplemented with Freya and/or Würzburg radars. As stations along the coast were sited with more or less equal spacing, this meant that they had to be adapted to the terrain and so there was no set plan for any particular type of station.

In general, during 1941-43, the stations only received the occasional harassing attack. RAF fighters, returning across the French coast from strafing targets inland, used up any remaining ammunition to shoot up these sites. Approaching from inland, flying low beneath radar cover, they could take the station defences of light anti-aircraft

Several versions were produced over the course of the war. Wurz-bürg A was operated manually and required the operator to pinpoint the target by maintaining a maximum signal on their oscilloscope display. The Model B added an infra-red detector but was not sucessful so was discontinued. Würzburg C was aimed by sending the signal out of one of two slightly off-centre horns in the middle of the antenna, the signal being switched rapidly between the two horns. The slight delay, displayed as two closely separated blips on the screen, produced better accuracy on a fast-moving target. Würzburg D had a conical scanning system which allowed it to move the dish in the direction on the maximum signal and hence track the target. All three models were fitted with IFF to identify friendly aircraft. It used a three-metre paraboloid dish antenna which could be folded in half for travel on its wheeler trailer.

weapons by surprise. The radar arrays, as a matter of operational necessity, were completely exposed for efficient reception. On the other hand, the grid-like structures could not be easily seen. A lack of German personnel skilled in electronics meant that station staff could not, in general, carry out repairs to their equipment, relying instead on mobile maintenance units allotted to various sectors of the coastline.

Apart from random attacks, there were two major assaults by Commandos on particular stations. The first was at Bruneval on the night of February 27/28, 1942 when a combined paratroop and seaborne force seized control while an RAF technician, Flight Sergeant Charles Cox, removed vital parts from the radar consoles to take back for examination by British scientists.

The second attack came the following August 19 during the combined attack on Dieppe. An offshoot of the operation was to obtain parts from the Dieppe/Caude-Côte radar station on the cliffs. Another RAF technician, Flight Sergeant Jack Nissenthal, escorted by Canadian troops, was tasked to examine the equipment as it

Above: **As the small dish models were not accurate enough to direct the laying of guns, so the Würzburg Riese (Giant) was developed with an attached cabin. Termed the FuMG 65, this had a 7.4-metre (24 feet) dish antenna giving a range of up to 70 kilometres (43 miles).** *Below:* **The interior of the Giant's cabin.**

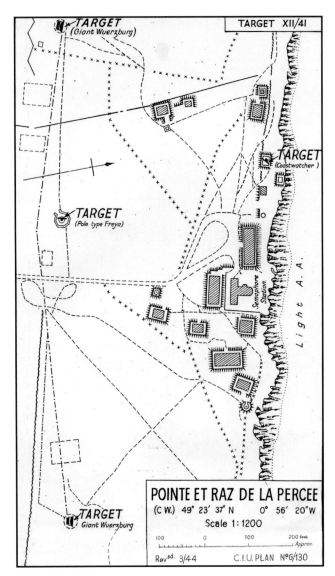

This example of the site plans drawn up by Medmenham shows Target 41 as at March 1944. (See also page 135.)

Unfortunately, this low-level oblique showing the destroyed Freya (arrowed) is not dated.

was deemed important to know if the Germans had access to the secret of the cavity magnetron valve that bestowed much greater range and accuracy. So important was this device that Nissenthal, aware of its purpose, could not be allowed to fall alive into enemy hands. If such an event seemed likely, his Canadian escort had orders to shoot him dead but fortunately he was able to return and report that the radar at Dieppe was conventional.

As a result of these Commando raids, radar stations along the coast were made into fortified positions. Hitherto there had only been fencing or wire to keep French civilians from observing too closely the apparatus in use. From late 1942, most had had a deep trench dug completely round the site except for portions where steep cliffs presented an obstacle. In addition, double wire fences were introduced to surround the sites. Labour was no problem as forced labour and Russian prisoners were available in large numbers from the Todt Organisation.

Throughout 1943 there were only a few attacks on the coastal stations. Also, to give effect of aid to Russia, by

exerting pressure on the Luftwaffe, Fighter Command was not always averse to their incursions over enemy

territory being detected as the object of fighter sweeps was to force the Luftwaffe into battle.

Above: **The Large Coastwatcher and Giant Wurzbürg at Cap de la Hève with its lighthouse just west of Le Havre, pictured at zero feet in the run-up to Operation 'Overlord'. This was Target 35 on** Medmenham's list (see overleaf) but by the end of the war it had been totally destroyed in the bombardments to capture the city. *Below:* **The two lighthouses were rebuilt in a different style.**

By early 1944 there were 61 known German radar stations between Belgium and Cap Fréhel. In the Pas-de-Calais area there was a coastal radar station on average every three miles, thinning out to about every five miles in Brittany.

Throughout the war Air Ministry Intelligence branches had watched the building and progress of these sites, taking in information culled by French Resistance members, SOE agents, photo-reconnaissance and captured documents. New radars were appearing, notably the Giant Würzburg (the German Würzburg-Riese) introduced for ground control interception stations. These large radars, sited on concrete bases, had turntables on which a large cabin was mounted. At each end of the cabin, trunnions supported the 24-foot diameter paraboloid that could be elevated as well as rotated. A larger Coastwatcher radar was introduced and a new pole-type Freya also came into use.

Then the new static long-range reporting radars were introduced with enormous arrays — the German Mammut — reported by the apt name 'Hoarding'. There was also a smaller version. Perhaps more impressive were the tall radars reported by the Allies as 'Chimneys', mounted on large concrete bases. There were of three types: box, cylinder and girder. These descriptive words were used for intelligence briefings for pilots as their German names were not then known. Most recognisable of the arrays was the Benito direction finding pylon, an open 65-foot wooden tower, at day fighter control stations.

FROM:- Headquarters, Sig.Int., A.E.A.F.

TO:- Int.9, A.E.A.F. *attn W/c Weaver*

REF:- AEAF/TS.16768/Int.

DATE:- 13th.April 1944.

SUBJECT:- Radar Targets.

The following Enemy Radar Thave been scheduled for destruction. Sites have been numbered in accordance with Rhubarb Appedix XII.

2. Scheduled for destruction between D-30 and D are Hoardings, Small Hoardings and Chimneys as follows:-

8. GRIS/NEZ/POINTE DU RIDEN	50 51 27N.01 35 06E.	SH.	
9. " "/BELLEVUE	50 51 31N.01 38 25E.	H	
13. BOULOGNE/MONUMENT	50 44 28N.00 36 52E.	O.	
27. DIEPPE/CAUDE-COTE	49 55 20N.01 02 52E.	H.	
39. CAEN DOUVRES	49 17 42N.00 24 17W.	C.	
46 CHERBOURG/LA BRASSERIE	49 40 05N. 01 28 09W.	C.	
49. CAP DE LA HAGUE/JOBOURG	49 41 10N.01 54 28W.	H.	
LE HAVRE D'OLLEMAND	49 31 32N.00 04 10E.	C under construction.	

3. Scheduled for destruction between D - 10 and D are all Giant Wuerzburg at sites 5, 18, 25, 26, 27, 28, 31, 32, 35, 38, 39, 40, 41, 48, 49. Particulars are given on this attached list under apparatus 'WR'. This list is merely a rewrite of the contents of Appendix XII for convenience of handling.

for Group Captain,
D/C.I.O.Sig.Int.,
Headquarters, A.E.A.F.

Above data without dates passed to targets section F/L Davies.

As D-Day approached, the main effort in the weeks preceding the invasion was against communication centres, railway bridges, locomotive sheds and canal locks. At the same time there was the need to implement the planning for the destruction of radar sites in the vicinity of the landing areas but, in the planning for the assault on the radars, there came a major diversion. Intelligence now having knowledge of the impending V-weapon attacks, with launching sites under constant air surveillance, this led the RAF into an all-out effort to disrupt the enemy's launching programme, fearing that it would affect the south coast assembly areas and shipping massing to convey troops across the Channel.

It was appreciated that the scale and variety of equipment employed by the German radar organisation was such that to seriously impair the system by air attack alone would be a formidable proposition. However, the destruction of certain vital radars and the comprehensive jamming of others could gravely interfere with the operation of the equipment. It was therefore decided to selectively attack and destroy radar stations between Ostend and the Channel Islands in accordance with the following principles: (a) Installations which could not be jammed electrically, or were difficult to jam; (b) Those stations capable of giving good readings on ships and for controlling coastal guns; (c) Stations that were likely to assist the enemy in inflicting casualties on airborne forces. It was also decided as part of the Cover Plan that two targets outside the assault area were to be attacked for every one attacked in the area. As this signal of April 13 shows, the targets selected for attack were selected from the Medmenham list *(opposite)*, a copy of which was attached to the letter. Attacks began on May 10 against the long-range aircraft reporting stations and on May 18 against those installations used for night fighter control and the control of coastal guns. Then, on May 25, a further 42 sites were scheduled for attack. These included 106 installations and by D minus 3, 14 were confirmed destroyed. Two enemy radio navigational stations important to the assault area at Sortosville and Lanmeur, and four wireless stations of the highest importance, were also targeted by RAF Bomber Command and claimed as being totally destroyed.

ENEMY COASTAL RADAR STATIONS.

SCHEDULE.

No.	Name.	Type.	Position	HT. ASL. FT.	Apparatus.
1.	YPRES/VOORMEZEELE	GCl.	50 48 39N. 02 52 39E.	90	2WR, F
2.	DUNKIRK/FORT DES DUNES	S.	51 03 15N. 02 26 52E.	20	WR.
3.	GRAVELINES/LE CLIPON	A/C.	51 01 34N. 02 12 25E.	20	2WR, 2F,W.
4.	GRAVELINES/PETIT FORT PHILLIPPE	S.	51 00 37N. 02 07 24E.	Sea.	WR. S.
× 5.	CAP BLANC NEZ	A/C.	50 55 47N. 01 42 52E.	300	2WR.F.
6.	CAP BLANC NEZ/ST.POL	S.	50 54 49N. 01 41 41E.	215	W (Coastal)
7.	CAP GRIS NEZ	S.	50 52 12N. 01 35 00E.	165	WR ?
8.	CAP GRIS NEZ/POINTE DU RIDEN	S.	50 51 27N. 01 35 06E.	170	SH, 2WR, W.
9.	CAP GRIS NEZ/BELLEVUE	A/C.	50 51 31N. 01 38 25E.	260	H, 2F.
10.	CAP GRIS NEZ/WATTERMEL ST.GEORGE	A/C.	50 51 42N. 01 37 43E.	150	WR.
11.	CAP GRIS NEZ/ONGLEVERT.	GC1	50 50 47N. 01 37 36E.	300	2WR, F, (F?)
12.	BOULOGNE/BOURSIN	D.	50 46 15N. 01 50 32E.	560	Benito.
13.	BOULOGNE/MONUMENT	A/C.	50 44 26N. 01 36 52E.	300	Ch (c)
14.	BOULOGNE/MONT LAMBERT	S.	50 43 09N. 01 39 07E.	600	S.
15A.	BOULOGNE/CAP D'ALPRECH	S.	50 41 57N. 01 33 44E.	140	WR,F, S.
15B.	BOULOGNE/CAP D'ALPRECH	S.	50 41 15N. 01 34 08E.	200	SH.
16.	BOULOGNE/HARDELOT	S.	50 39 04N. 01 34 51E.	80	W.
17.	MONT VIOLETTE	A/C.	50 37 22N. 01 40 34E.	585	F.
×18.	NEUFCHATEL/MONT ST.FRIEUX.	S.	50 36 37 N 01 36 25E.	330	WR.
19.	LE TOUQUET/PLAGE ST.CECILY	A/C.	50 34 26N. 01 34 42E.	23	2WR,F, W.
20.	FRUGES/PREDEFIN	A/C.	50 29 39N. 02 15 02E.	520	H, 2WR,F.
21.	AUBIGNY/FREVILLERS	D.	50 24 39N. 02 31 09E.	625	5 Benito
22.	BERCK-SUR-MER.	S.	50 24 04N. 01 33 26E.	20	S.
23.	CAYEUX/NOUVEAU BRIGTHON	S.	50 11 47N. 01 30 42E.	Sea	WR.
24.	AMIENS/MONTRELET.	GCl.	50 05 04N. 02 12 33E.	460	2WR,F, W.
× 25.	ABBEVILLE/VAUDRICOURT	A/C.	50 07 16N. 01 31 55E.	165	Ch (c) 2WR,2F,W.
× 26.	LE TREPORT/MONT HUON	S.	50 03 29N 01 21 38E.	330	WR, S.
×27.	DIEPPE/CAUDE-COTE	A/C.	49 55 20N. 01 02 52E.	195	H,2WR,2F W.
× 28.	ST.VALERY-EN-CAUX/MANNEVILLE ES PLAINS A/C		49 51 55N. 00 45 20E.	250	2WR, 2F.
29.	ST.VALERY-EN-CAUX/ST.MARTIN AUX BUNAUX D.		49 50 18N. 00 33 39E.	280	Benito.
30.	FECAMP/CHAPELLE DE LA VIERGE	S.	49 46 07N. 00 22 13E.	380	SH, WR, 2S.
×31.	CAP D'ANTIFER/SEMAPHORE	S.	49 41 10N. 00 09 55E.	330	WR, S.
×32.	CAP D'ANTIFER	A/C.	49 40 45N. 00 09 46E.	350	Ch(c)2F,WR.
33.	YVETOT/EPINAY SUR DUCLAIR	GC1.	49 31 18N. 00 51 11E.	350	2 WR, F.
34.	NEUFCHATEL/SULLY	GC1.	49 32 55N. 01 45 47E.	700	2WR, F.
×35.	LE HAVRE/CAP DE LA HEVE	S.	49 30 42N. 00 04 00E.	340	S. large S.
36.	LISIEUX/LE THEIL NOLENT	GCl.	49 09 41N. 00 32 52E.	600	2 WR.F.
37.	BERNAY/LA CHALIERE	D.	49 05 00N. 00 27 00E.	620	5 Benito.
×38.	HOULGATE/SEMAPHORE	S.	49 18 22N. 00 03 45W.	375	WR.
× 39.	CAEN/DOUVRES LA DELIVERANDE	A/C.	49 17 13N. 00 24 24W.	265	Ch(b) 2WR, F.
×40.	ARROMANCHES	S.	49 20 25N. 00 36 57W.	200	WR.S.
×41.	POINTE ET RAZ DE LA PERCEE	S.	49 23 37N. 00 56 20W.	100	2WR.S, F.
42.	ST.LO/BOURG D'ENFER	D.	49 08 47N. 01 03 21W.	380	3 Benito.
43.	VIRE/LE PARC	GCl.	48 49 39N. 00 45 09W.	720	2WR, F.
44.	BARFLEUR/LE VICEL.	S.	49 37 30N. 01 18 15W.	345	S(large), WR.
45.	CHERBOURG/CAP LEVY	S.	49 41 41N. 01 28 12W.	50	S, WR.
46.	CHERBOURG/FERMANVILLE (LA BRASSERIE)A/C.		49 40 05N. 01 28 10W.	450	Ch (c) 2WR,F.
47.	OMONVILLE LA ROGUE/ASSELINS	S.	49 42 19N. 01 51 28W.	230	S large SH,
× 48.	CAP DE LA HAGUE/AUDERVILLE	A/C.	49 42 52N. 01 56 02W.	165	2WR, 2F,F(large)
×49.	CAP DE LA HAGUE/JOBOURG	A/C.	49 41 07N. 01 54 28W.	550	H,WR.
50.	CAP DE CARTERET/SEMEPHORE	S.	49 22 28N. 01 48 23W.	220	S.
51.	GUERNSEY/FORT GEORGE	A/C.	49 26 46N. 02 32 19W.	300	WR,2F, WR,S?.
52.	GUERNSEY/PLEINEMONT	S.	49 26 05N. 02 40 24W.	150.	F.
53.	JERSEY/ROUGE NEZ.	S.	49 15 18N. 02 14 59W.	225	F.
54.	ST.MALO/POINTE DU GROUIN	S.	48 42 42N. 01 50 36W.	90	S, W.
55.	CAP FREHEL	A/C.	48 40 49N. 02 19 02W.	165	H,2WR, 3F.
56.	MONCONTOUR/BEL AIR	D.	48 19 22N 02 35 05W.	1130	5 Benito.
57.	LOUDEAC/LA RECOMPENSE	GC1.	48 14 16N 02 41 40W.	910	2WR, 2F.
58.	MONTERFIL/LES EPINAIS	GCI.	48 03 27N. 02 00 37W.	320	2WR,F.
59.	VITRE/LA HAYE	GCI.	48 03 01N. 01 17 09W.	300	2WR, F.
60.	OISSEAU/MARETRE	GCI.	48 21 39N. 00 38 46W.	440	2WR,F.
61.	FALAISE/RI	GCI.	48 47 26N. 00 08 44W.	720	2WR, F?.

GCI= Night Fighter Control   W= Wuerzburg. S = ShipWatcher (Seetakt)
A/C= A/C Reporting Radar   WR= Giant Wuerzburg Ch(b)=Chimney (Box Type)
S= Ship   "   "   F= Freya   Ch(c)= " (Celinder type)
Day Fighter Control   H= Hoarding   ?= Site for apparatus.
SH= Small Hoarding

For the Operation 'Neptune' plan see overleaf.

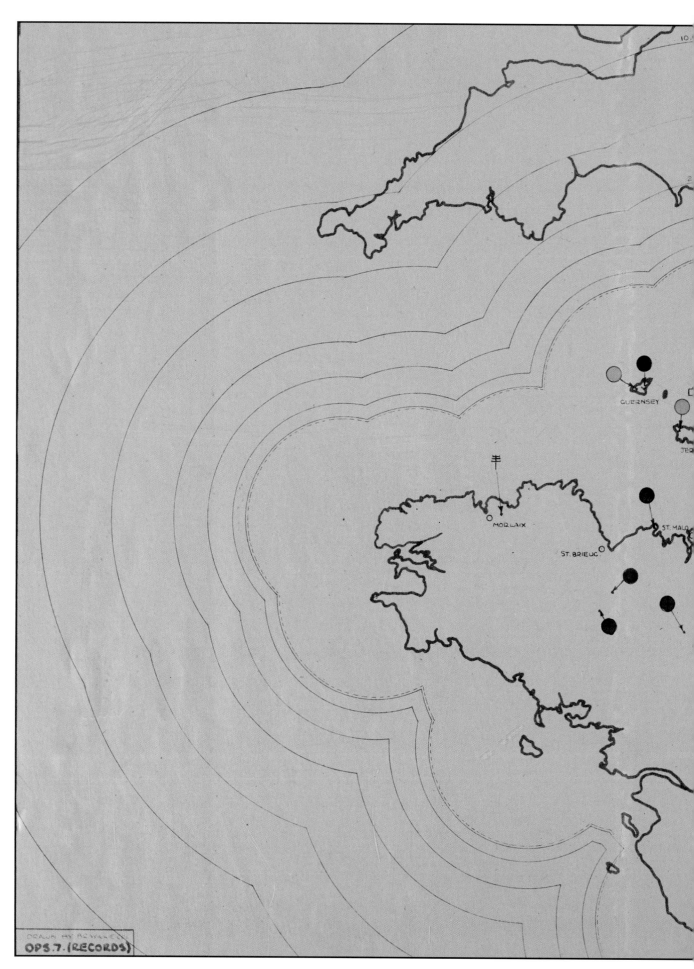

Labels visible on map: GUERNSEY, JER..., MORLAIX, ST. MALO, ST. BRIEUC

The extent of German radar cover, according to Allied intelligence, is illustrated on this plan. Ground Control Interception sites

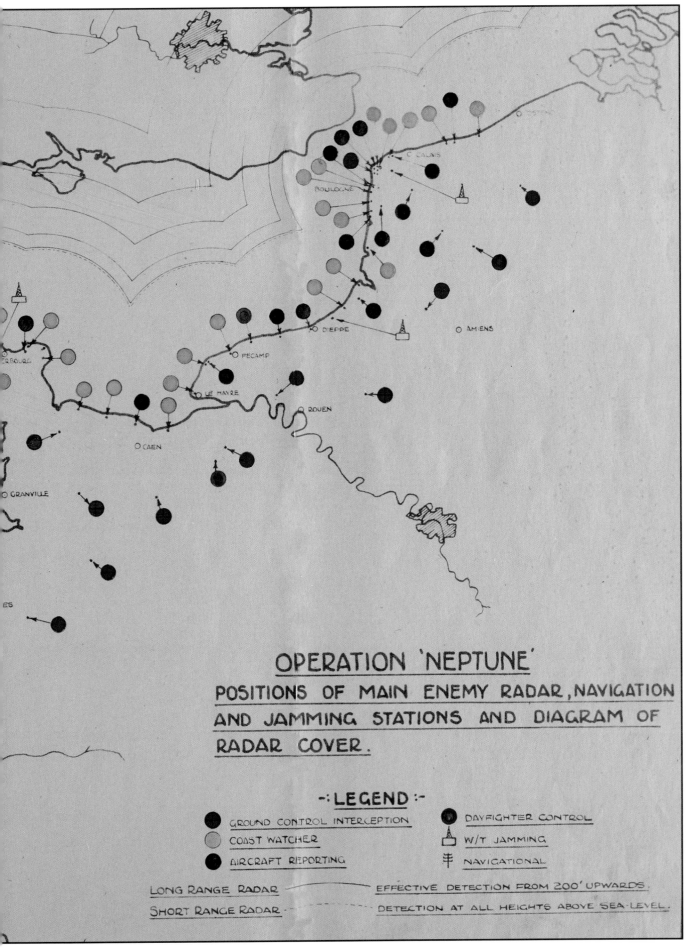

OPERATION 'NEPTUNE'
POSITIONS OF MAIN ENEMY RADAR, NAVIGATION AND JAMMING STATIONS AND DIAGRAM OF RADAR COVER.

-: LEGEND :-

- GROUND CONTROL INTERCEPTION
- COAST WATCHER
- AIRCRAFT REPORTING
- DAYFIGHTER CONTROL
- W/T JAMMING
- NAVIGATIONAL

LONG RANGE RADAR ——————— EFFECTIVE DETECTION FROM 200' UPWARDS

SHORT RANGE RADAR -- -- -- -- DETECTION AT ALL HEIGHTS ABOVE SEA-LEVEL.

marked in red, Coastwatcher stations in yellow and Aircraft Reporting stations in blue. Day Fighter Control sites are green.

A Würzburg at an unspecified location pictured during the winter of 1942.

This resulted in the task of putting out the enemy's eyes being given mainly to fighters of the Second Tactical Air Force destined to operate from French soil once sufficient territory had been captured. Spitfires and Typhoons of Nos. 83 and 84 Groups were chiefly concerned in attacking the radar sites with low-level cannon and rocket fire. US fighters of the Eighth and Ninth Air Forces were also briefed to play a part although these operations could not be phased over a long period. With D-Day planned for June 5 (in the event put back one day due to adverse weather reports), it was essential that attacks only took place shortly before that date so that repairs could not be effected before the landings took place or allow time for the Germans to organise mobile radars to fill in gaps in their coverage.

In the same way that the Germans had decoy airfields, so there were dummy radar arrays inviting attack, some being reported by French Resistance members who noted the lack of cabling. One dummy 'Hoarding' was erected a mile north-east of the Fruges aircraft reporting station, made conspicuous by square blocks of concrete either side.

Another method of 'blinding' the enemy radars was jamming by both ground stations and airborne equipment. To this, the Germans countered with various anti-jamming devices. The Würzburgs, designed to operate on a narrow frequency band, were modified to a spread of two, then three bands.

Then a continuous tuning device, code-named 'Michael', permitted a more rapid switching of bands and made it possible to alter the frequency while operating. German stations reported serious jamming from early 1944 and jamming over the whole sector nearest to Britain from mid-April.

One of the first Typhoon attacks in the intensive phase was on Caen/Douvres-la-Délivrande by Nos. 198 and 609 Squadrons. Diving from 6,000 feet, releasing their rockets at around 1,500 feet, hits were observed around the aerial displays and the target was left covered in smoke. Twelve Typhoons from No. 198 Squadron were also put up to attack one of the two radar stations at St Valéry-en-Caux. Flying in at sea level, they rose to 6,000 feet to cross the enemy coast west of the target for their diving attack. One mast was seen to collapse to the ground. Wing Commander Richard Brooker's aircraft leading the attack was hit by flak on the way out forcing him to bale out and take to his dinghy. His Number 2, Squadron Leader Denis Sweeting, sent out a Mayday call and within an hour Brooker had been picked up by a Walrus.

	RHUBARB XIII JAMMERS							File 16768 17A
TOP SECRET			Pinpoints.				Grid Ref:	Ft. Above Sea Level
1.	Dieppe/Berneval le Grand Jammer Site.	49	57	45 N	01	11	26 E	313718	350
2.	Fecamp/Chappelle de la Vierge. D/F Site.	49	46	07 N	0	22	53 E	713556	350
3.	Cherbourg/Urville-Hague. Jammer Site & Y Organisation	49	40	18 N	1	44	21 E	059271	300
4.	Beaumont-Hague/Au Fevre. Jammer Site.	49	40	34 N	01	46	23 W	035277	285
5.	Cherbourg/St.Croix-Hague. D/F Site	49	38	17 N	01	47	00 W	026235	550

Five sites were singled out for jamming.

20

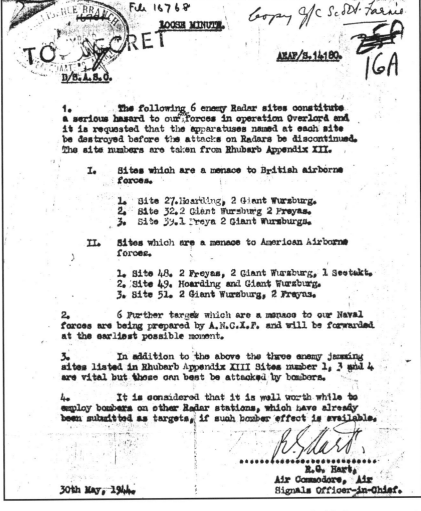

1.   The following 6 enemy Radar sites constitute a serious hazard to our forces in operation Overlord and it is requested that the apparatuses named at each site be destroyed before the attacks on Radars be discontinued. The site numbers are taken from Rhubarb Appendix XII.

    I.   Sites which are a menace to British airborne forces.

       1.   Site 27. Hoarding, 2 Giant Wurzburg.
       2.   Site 32. 2 Giant Wurzburg 2 Freyas.
       3.   Site 39. 1 Freya 2 Giant Wurzburgs.

    II.   Sites which are a menace to American Airborne forces.

       1.   Site 48. 2 Freyas, 2 Giant Wurzburg, 1 Seetakt.
       2.   Site 49. Hoarding and Giant Wurzburg.
       3.   Site 51. 2 Giant Wurzburg, 2 Freyas.

2.   6 Further targets which are a menace to our Naval forces are being prepared by A.N.C.X.F. and will be forwarded at the earliest possible moment.

3.   In addition to the above the three enemy jamming sites listed in Rhubarb Appendix XIII Sites number 1, 3 and 4 are vital but those can best be attacked by bombers.

4.   It is considered that it is well worth while to employ bombers on other Radar stations, which have already been submitted as targets, if such bomber effect is available.

                                      R.G. Hart,
                               Air Commodore, Air
30th May, 1944.   Signals Officer-in-Chief.

To conserve the effort, just three days before D-Day, it was decided to concentrate attacks on the 12 most important sites, six to be chosen by the naval authorities and six selected by the air commanders. This minute confirms the instruction, but on May 30 the Allied Naval Command had still not submitted their six chosen targets. Although it was very late in the day, the official log states that attacks on all the sites, comprising 39 installations, had been carried out before the invasion commenced.

markers were red with green sparks. Such elaborate display of pyrotechnics was necessary as with sky marking, the Germans might well send up spoof parachute flares away from the actual target. Not surprisingly this attack was not a success so it was repeated two nights later when good visibility permitted controlled Oboe marking by Mosquitos. This station, consisting of W/T masts placed diagonally across an old fort and control buildings 150 yards to the south, was completely destroyed.

On June 4 the Cap d'Antifer radar station was attacked by 23 Spitfires from Nos. 441, 442 and 443 Squadrons of the Royal Canadian Air Force, achieving five direct hits with 500lb bombs.

In all, 46 radar stations were targeted in the immediate run-up to D-Day, some being attacked more than once with Pointe et Raz de la Percée three times. Its Freya was destroyed by rockets and both Würzburgs were hit by machine-gun fire. Bomb bursts on the telephone exchange and an emergency radio installation temporarily isolated the unit so that the mobile repair facility could not be contacted. On D-Day their Würzburgs were further damaged by naval gun-fire.

The vital radars at Arromanches also sustained three attacks. In the first raid, by Mustangs and Thunderbolts of the Ninth Air Force, both the Coastwatcher and Würzburg were put out of action and some of the crews were wounded. In this case repairs were immediately put in hand. Broken instruments were not a serious set-back, but severed cables were troublesome. Two Telefunken experts were called in from Boulogne, and while Coastwatcher array was repaired by welding that took three days, the severed cable could not be replaced. During the subsequent attacks the crews prudently took to their shelters some 40 feet below ground.

In spite of their programme of disrupting transportation and destroying coastal gun batteries, from May 10 RAF Bomber Command also assisted in the blinding of the radar sites by bombing reporting stations inland before switching to night fighter control stations. Bomber Command was also tasked with blocking the enemy's ears. On the night of May 31/June 1, a mixed force of 109 Halifaxes and 16 Lancasters set out to bomb the coastal wireless transmitting station of Au Fèvre. Two of its six high masts were brought down and others damaged. Of the two main buildings, one received a direct hit on a blast wall and the other was surrounded by near misses.

That same night another mixed force, comprised of 115 Lancasters and Halifaxes, with Pathfinder Mosquitos, were despatched to destroy the wireless station at Mont Couple near Boulogne that housed some 60 transmitters.

On the night of June 1/2, 100-plus Halifaxes, with Mosquito marking, attempted to eliminate the Ferme d'Urville wireless station but, thwarted by cloud, bombing had to be attempted by sky markers. In this instance the

Up to D-Day, 1,668 sorties were flown by aircraft of the Allied Expeditionary Air Force against radar installations. Typhoons in low-level attacks flew 694 sorties and fired 4,517 × 60lb rocket projectiles. Typhoons and Spitfires made 759 dive-bombing sorties, dropping 1,258 × 500lb bombs, and light and medium bombers dropped 218 tons of bombs. In addition, the sites were sprayed with many thousands of rounds of cannon and machine-gun fire.

The Würzburgs at Arromanches were finally brought back into operation late on the night of June 5/6. In the early hours of June 6 they detected the formations of Dakotas carrying paratroops for the initial D-Day assault. Having no type identification facility, they were reported as a bomber stream heading inland, a matter that did not concern the coastal defences!

On June 5, a final attack was made on the Cap de la Hague/Jobourg station by rocket-firing Typhoons of Nos. 174, 175 and 245 Squadrons.

While attacks on the Normandy coast invasion areas were vital, even heavier attacks had been made on radar stations in the Pas-de-Calais area under the overall deception plan that the main assault would be made in that area. It was also important that attacks against stations near Cap d'Antifer were only partly effective to allow detection of the spoof invasion force.

Under Operation 'Taxable', Lancasters of No. 617 Squadron dropped Window while flying a complicated 'counter-marching' pattern, lateral to the French coast, but nearing it gradually to create the impression on enemy radars of a seaborne force approaching at seven knots on a 14-mile front. This was in phase with 18 small ships with reflectors to give the impression of large ships. This ruse had the desired effect while the landings in Normandy took place.

After D-Day, a number of the German coastal radar stations continued to operate until overrun by Allied troops. Those still functioning were heavily jammed as the build-up following D-Day continued. On June 20 the 13. Kompanie of Luft-Nachrichten-Regiment 53, numbering some 160 men, manning the Cap de la Hague/Auderville station, were ordered to destroy the installation. This was blown up and the unit ordered to report to an Oberst-

A Giant Würzburg, probably one from the station at Cherbourg/Fermanville (Target 46), shortly after its capture by US forces in June 1944.

leutnant Keil, in charge of the defence of a coastal sector, to act as infantry. However, they ended up with Keil as prisoners of the Americans!

Air Intelligence had received information of a new long-range radar being used by the Germans called Jagdschloss (Hunting Castle). This embodied advances that hitherto had been exclusive to Allied radars. With a 90-mile range, it was thought to be German intentions to build a back-up chain

Left: **This was the radar sited at Cap Blanc-Nez (see page 60) about two miles south-west of the Lindemann battery at Sangatte.** Right: **When the battery was captured in September there** was not much left of the Giant Würzburg that once stood on the roof of the battery plotting room and command post. Today this whole site has been buried under spoil from the Channel Tunnel.

inland across France although this was thwarted by the speed of the Allied advance. They were eventually installed in the German homeland and in Norway, and by late 1944 seven Jagdschloss radars had been pinpointed: Ringsted, Darmstadt, Fehmarn, Stuttgart, Siegen, Rosemart and Wünsdorf.

By September 1944 all the German radar stations in France and Belgium had been abandoned with the equipment in the operating cabins and buildings smashed. Later American forces, working with the French, assisted in clearing the sites. The first consideration was the clearance of unexploded bombs before the aerial arrays could be dismantled.

The French, anxious to dispose of evidence of enemy occupation, tried enthusiastically to obliterate all traces of the installations, but concrete bases were more difficult to dispose of so that in post-war years, cement plinths were as common in Northern France coastal areas as pillboxes in south and eastern England. At Dieppe/Caude-Côte, one radar installation was toppled over the cliffs where it remained on the shore for many years.

RAF Disarmament Wings, working in the British Zone of Germany and Norway, received little from the French coastal sites. One Giant Würzburg, mounted on a railway truck, was despatched to the UK for research, and four Würzburgs were sent to England to be allotted as station trophies by the Air Historical Branch of the Air Ministry, but they appear to have been treated in the same way as the Branch's holding of a Hampden bomber: scrapped! A num-

Most of the Freyas, being basically a lattice framework, were scrapped after the war but a good specimen survives at the observatory at Ondrejov in the Czech Republic.

ber of smaller items such as consols and cathode ray tubes were sent to the German Air Force Equipment Centre at Stanmore. As representative of the many Freyas mounted along the French coast, one early example reached RAE Farnborough. This was Freya Limber No. 1 found at the Felzerhaken naval radar station. Built in 1935, it was said to have been demonstrated to Hitler in 1943.

Years later a single Giant Würzburg was rescued from a scrap heap by Professor Sir Martin Ryle for use, first as a radar telescope and later as an interference tracing receiver, but by 1979 it suffered from lack of spares. Other Würzburgs were secured by scientific bodies in Europe, the one at the radar museum at Douvres in Normandy (see page 132) being supplied by the Observatoire de Paris.

Of the 1,500 Giant Würzburgs produced during the war, several remain to be seen today. This one, originally at Pardubice Airport in the Czech Republic, was moved to Ondrejov in 1957-58 to be modified for tracking meteorites. It remained in service until 2006.

The Bruneval Raid

By Alfred Price

The French coast under the watchful eye of RAF photo-reconnaissance in June 1940. This is Saint-Jouin-Bruneval which was located some 20 kilometres along the coast north of Le Havre.

It all began in 1940. Although the Germans had achieved a mighty victory in France, at the same time it made them more vulnerable as they now had to protect a vastly enlarged western frontier. Consequently, they began the installation of a chain of radar stations, of which those bordering the English Channel were the most important.

By the spring of 1941, the existence of an effective German early-warning radar network called Freya, operating on 125 megacycles, was accepted by British scientists. By the end of October, the locations of 27 'radio direction finding' stations had been plotted from Bodo in Norway to Bordeaux in France. At the same time, different radar signals of 570 megacycles had been picked up but the new device defied all attempts to locate it.

However late in November 1941, Dr Charles Frank, a physicist on the staff of Dr Reginald Jones (a brilliant scientist attached to the Air Ministry Directorate of Intelligence, better known simply as R. V. Jones), was examining a medium-level photograph of the Freya station at Bruneval on the northern coast of France near Le Havre, when he noticed that a track had been trodden out along the cliff-edge. This ran from

On the cliff top, a Parisian dentist owned this charming holiday home (circled on the aerial photo) but it was quickly expropriated by the Germans to be used as a barracks for the operators of one of the dozens of radio-location stations being set up all along the coast.

Reproduced from GSGS No. 4042, 1943

the Freya aerials towards a large house that appeared to be some sort of headquarters building. Just before it reached the building, the track swung round to the right, and ended at a small black object about half-way between the house and the cliffs with their sheer drop to the sea. Somebody had considered it worth his while to tread out a path from the main radar station to this object. Could it be that the black object played some part in the working of the Freya?

On December 3, Flight Lieutenant Tony Hill, a reconnaissance pilot, chanced to visit the photographic inter-

Flight Lieutenant Antony Hill of No. 1 Photographic Reconnaissance Unit based at Benson, Oxfordshire, was instrumental in taking low-level photographs of the site in December 1941 having been told it was of great importance as it was believed to be the source of radar transmissions on a new frequency. The suspected Würzburg installation is arrowed.

pretation centre at Medmenham in Buckinghamshire. Hill had come to discuss the low-level photography of the German radar sites with Squadron Leader Claude Wavell and, because Wavell knew of Frank's special interest in the Bruneval radar site, he mentioned the object to Hill.

On the following day, on his own initiative, Hill took off in his Spitfire to go and have a look at Bruneval. He swept in low over the cliffs, and was past the emplacement and out over the trees behind it before the startled defenders knew what had happened. On his return, Hill discovered that his camera had failed to function properly but he had still seen the device clearly — it looked like 'an electric bowl-fire and about ten feet across'. If Hill was right this was almost certainly the elusive source of the 570-megacycle transmissions.

The German unit stationed there was the 23. Kompanie of the V. Abteilung of Luftgau-Nachrichten-Regiment Westfrankreich.

The next day, Flight Lieutenant Hill repeated his performance and the photographs he brought back were among the classics of the war as they showed the radar device exactly as he had described it. However, a photograph was only half the story; it still remained to be proved that the instrument transmitted on 570 megacycles. Until this had been proven, counter-measures could not begin.

As the radar station lay within 200 yards of the coast, by the beginning of January 1942 an operation to Bruneval to inspect and hopefully retrieve components from the radar was receiving detailed consideration. However, it soon became clear that a commando raid from the sea would be doomed to failure as the site was situated at the top of high cliffs, no doubt protected by a sizeable German garrison. Even if the raiders could have fought their way to the top of the cliffs without suffering crippling casualties, it was unlikely in the extreme that they could do so before the defenders destroyed the installation.

However, it was undoubtedly this beautiful photograph brought back by Tony, showing the dish aerial located in a separate pit between the house and the cliff edge, that led Dr Jones to propose that the station should be raided to capture the secrets of the radar installation.

Using the aerial photos, RAF Medmenham produced this model to be used to brief C Company of the 2nd Parachute Battalion which had been chosen to carry out Operation 'Biting'.

Left: Commanding the 120-strong airborne force was Major John Frost (right). With him is Lieutenant-Colonel John Goschen, the Quartermaster of the fledgling Airborne Division.

Leading the aircraft transporting the paratroops to France was pipe-smoking Wing Commander Charles Pickard, seen here inspecting a German helmet after the operation had taken place.

Instead, Lord Louis Mountbatten, in charge of Combined Operations, suggested that parachute troops should be used. On January 21, the Chiefs-of-Staff agreed and ordered that one company of paratroops, sufficient light naval craft to evacuate the force by sea and an operational squadron of Whitley bombers to transport the paratroops be made available. The venture was given the code-name 'Biting'.

'C' Company of the 2nd Parachute Battalion was chosen for the operation. The unit began training for what they were told would be 'a special demonstration exercise, which will probably take place in the Isle of Wight, and the whole of the War Cabinet will be there to see it'.

While the military side of the operation was proceeding, Dr Jones was devoting thought to the intelligence aspect of the attack. By this time, he had learned that the 'bowl-fire' was in fact a radar called Würzburg, and that such a set had been erected near the Bruneval Freya station. This latter confirmation had come in an agent's report. Colonel André Neufinck (code-name 'Pol') had visited Bruneval in January with the help of the local French resistance agent Charles Chauveau (code-name 'Charlemagne'), a garage proprietor in Le Havre 20 kilometres away. What still remained to be proven was that Würzburg was the source of the 570-megacycle transmissions, and for this to be resolved it was necessary for somebody to remove the aerial from the centre of the 'bowl'. In case all else failed, a radio receiver was to be carried in one of the naval craft dispatched to evacuate the raiders from the beach, and this receiver would be used to establish whether any 570-megacycle transmissions could be heard coming from the station.

The next objective was the capture of the Würzburg's receiver and its associated presentation, or 'display', equipment. These would reveal whether the Germans had built any anti-jamming circuitry into the set. The transmitter was also wanted, so that British scientists could form some impression of the German techniques on frequencies as high as 570 megacycles. Dr Jones also asked for two prisoners to be taken — radar operators if possible — so that information could be obtained on the German methods of operating the radar and aircraft reporting. Finally, as all German signals equipment bore highly informative labels and inspection stamps, and a great deal of useful general intelligence could probably be obtained from these, Jones requested that should the various units prove impossible to unlodge, at least their labels should be torn off for him.

The Whitleys were supplied by No. 51 Squadron which had also been involved in Britain's very first paratroop raid back in February 1941 to blow the aqueduct across the Tragino river in Italy (see *After the Battle* No. 81). Based at Dishforth in Yorkshire, now in February 1942 a detachment of 12 Whitleys was sent to Andover for training for the Bruneval raid. Group Captain Sir Nigel Norman was in overall charge of the RAF element of the operation. He originally commanded the Central Landing Establishment at RAF Ringway, developing airborne troops, before becoming the AOC of No. 38 Wing (later No. 38 Group).

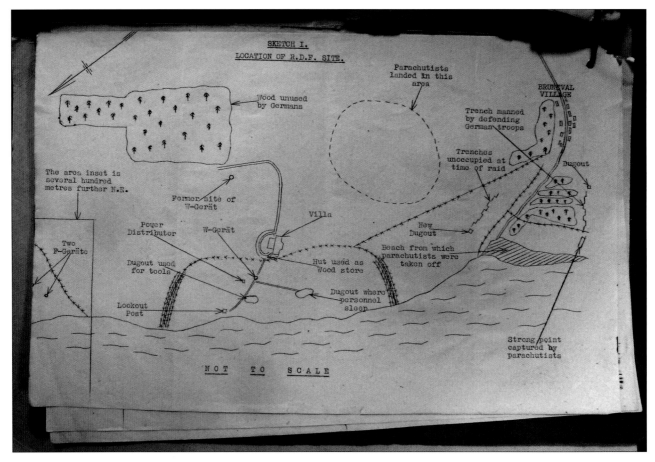

SKETCH I.
LOCATION OF R.D.F. SITE.

This plan from a post-raid intelligence report illustrates the layout of the Bruneval site.

The actual dismembering of the Würzburg equipment would be undertaken by seven men of the Royal Engineers, commanded by Lieutenant Dennis Vernon. There was to be an eighth man in the team who was not a soldier at all: Flight Sergeant Charles Cox, an RAF radar mechanic, was to go along just in case any specialist knowledge was required.

The dismantling party was given a British gun-laying radar — the nearest equivalent to the Würzburg — on which to practise, and they demonstrated considerable skill. Vernon and Cox were given a special briefing on the expected character and layout of the German set.

According to the raid's planned timetable, they would have barely half an hour with the apparatus. They had to be trained to make sketches and take photographs of the equipment in this time, and then to dismantle it systematically, beginning at the aerial and working backwards through the receiver to the presentation gear.

By the fourth week in February all was ready but now the weather intervened. On the evening of the 24th the weather was unsuitable, and it was again unsuitable on the 25th and the 26th. The timing of the raid was extremely critical as the attack had to take place on the night of a full moon, but at the same time the tide would have to be on the rise otherwise the assault craft would be left stranded on the beach. The 27th was the last possible date for a month or more but

fortunately the weather forecast was favourable for that evening. Thus informed, the Commander-in-Chief Portsmouth, Admiral Sir William James, signalled: 'Carry out Operation "Biting" tonight 27th February'.

Just before ten o'clock that evening, 12 converted Whitley bombers of No. 51 Squadron took off from Thruxton near Andover, loaded with 119 paratroops. One of those on board later wrote that 'the mugs of hot tea (well laced with rum) we had drunk before taking off began to scream to be let out. In that restricted space and encumbered as we were there was, alas, no way.'

It was a two-hour flight out to the dropping zone. At a quarter-past midnight on the morning of the 28th, the first sticks of paratroops leapt from their aircraft to land on a carpet of virgin snow, 600 yards to the south of the radar site. Their arrival had passed unnoticed as the sound of the Whitleys' engines faded into the night.

The men assembled in small groups and there were whispered orders but the next move was not a warlike one for that tea just had to go! Major John Frost, the force's commander, later wrote that this 'was certainly not good drill, as now was the time when a stick of parachutists was most vulnerable . . . but at least it was a gesture of defiance!'

According to the pre-arranged plan, the force split into three parties. The first section, code-named 'Nelson', commanded by Lieutenant Euan Charteris was to move to the beach to secure it for the withdrawal. However, Charteris

failed to arrive at the forming-up point and the Lieutenant's No. 2, Captain John Ross, in command of the heavy weapons section, was asked by Major Frost to proceed without him.

The second party itself split into three groups. 'Jellicoe' group under Lieutenant Peter Young was to move straight to the radar installation (code-named 'Henry') followed by the Royal Engineers dismantling party when it was safe to do so. Major Frost would personally lead 'Hardy' group to capture the château (code-named 'Lone House') whilst Lieutenant Peter Naumoff, commanding 'Drake' section, would take up a position between Le Presbytère Farm (code-named 'Rectangle' and where a hundred or so Germans were billeted), and the château.

The third group, 'Rodney', under Lieutenant John Timothy, was to act as defence against attack from the inland side.

Whilst the 'Hardy' section silently surrounded the château. Major Frost stole round to the front door which, to his surprise, was wide open. Satisfied that all was ready for battle to begin: he gave the signal for battle to begin: four blasts on his whistle.

With four men at his heels, Major Frost entered the building. The ground floor was dirty and empty but gun-fire could be heard coming from upstairs. They ran upstairs and, finding a solitary German firing on Lieutenant Young's 'Jellicoe' party around the radar aerial, promptly killed him.

It was decided that someone with technical knowledge of radar should go on the raid to be able to identify which components from the Würzburg should be removed. Both Derrick Garrard of the Telecommunications Research Establishment and Jones volunteered but were refused as they were in possession of too much secret information should they be captured, although one member of TRE was present with the naval force that was detailed to evacuate the paras and the radar equipment after the raid. However, there was still a need for someone knowledgeable from the RAF's radar mechanics to supervise and Flight Sergeant Charles Cox, a former cinema projectionist, volunteered but he was not told to what he had committed himself! Jones realised that if Cox was captured his RAF uniform would single him out for special attention so he tried — unsuccessfully — to get the War Office to issue him with an army uniform. Instead, Jones gave him advice on what to say at any interrogation and to be wary of any German officer who appeared to be kind. To this Cox replied: 'I can stand a lot of kindness, Sir!'

Here Group Captain Norman discusses the success of the operation with Flight Sergeant Cox on the deck of HMS *Prince Albert* at Portsmouth. (As a renowned aviator and founder of Heston Airport, Norman was killed in a crash at St Eval in May 1943.)

I met Mr Vernon [Lieutenant Don Vernon] at forming-up point at approximately 12.35. We proceeded under his direction to pull trolleys up towards house over various barbedwire defences and through snow, which was rather rough going.

In about 200 yards Mr Vernon went on to house and said we must make our way to left-hand side of house and conceal ourselves until he whistled or shouted for us. This we did, and lay in a small ridge for what seemed to be quite a long while but was really a very short time. Then one of the Sappers went over and said we must go through and meet up with the equipment immediately. Then we all went forward and through some more barbed wire to the equipment. I saw Mr Vernon and he said: 'This is it!'.

The barbed wire was not more than two feet high, a criss-cross network about 10 feet thick. Range of distance round equipment about a radius of 50 yards.

In view of the obstacles, it would have been better to have made arrangements for carrying the equipment and tools, etc. in haversacks, rather than on trolleys.

I surveyed the apparatus and found it to my surprise just like the photograph. The first point of interest was the aerial, which I looked at, and one of the Sappers proceeded to cut it from its centre. I went round the back, tracing the aerial lead to the top box of the paraboloid. A compartment behind the paraboloid contained a big box at the top with two smaller boxes underneath. On the right-hand side of the small boxes was a panel of push buttons, and at the base of the compartment was something that appeared to be a large metal rectifier although this had round fins instead of square.

I then proceeded to attack the equipment with the tools to try to get it out without damaging it. This proved unsuccessful except in one case that

came away easily, so we proceeded to rip the rest of the stuff out by sheer force. By this time the soldiers were getting impatient, and we were told to withdraw.

During the whole period of working at the equipment, bullets were flying much too close to be pleasant, but while we were working at the back of the paraboloid we were protected by the metal of the paraboloid itself.

After the war Charles Cox's exploit rather faded from view yet he still appeared at anniversary occasions. He died in 1997. Professor Jones wrote in his book *Most Secret War* that he tried hard to have Cox (who went on the raid under the name of 'Private Newman' in case he was captured) awarded either the Distinguished Conduct Medal or the Distinguished Flying Medal, the latter being the Air equivalent of the Military Medal. But Jones said that protocol would not allow it, so with Sergeants David Grieve and Gregor MacKenzie, Cox was awarded the Military Medal. Major Frost and Lieutenant Charteris received the Military Cross.

I noticed on the paraboloid before the aerial was cut out, on the left-hand side slightly above centre, the letters W.D. and a row of lines, horizontal lines arranged in a vertical scale, and against each line was a number about an inch apart.

The whole of the equipment was very solidly made and turned on its base with the slightest pressure. All leads were sealed into it in concentric plugs and sockets. The aerial socket ended in a type of attachment known to us as a Niphan plug. The mounting was not on wheels but looked as if it had been mounted on wheels and the wheels had been removed. There was no barbed wire on the boxes surrounding the equipment.

We retired when the Army told us, and we found that the equipment could be carried much better on our shoulders than by the trolley, so the trolley was abandoned. On coming down the slope we were met by a hail of machinegun fire from the opposite side of the cliff and we tried to dig ourselves in. Mr Vernon told me to take charge of the Sappers while he went back with the rearguard. We lay on the bank for about 15 mins, and then received a hail from the village that the beach defences had been taken. We made our way down the slope to the beach and found we had to wait so we stowed the equipment in a safe position under the cliff, and as there was nothing else we could do, we just sat down and waited.

After about half an hour the Navy came and we got the equipment aboard, with the wounded, and after the rearguard had time to make the beach and get into the boats, we pushed off. Slight enemy fire was directed against us from the cliff tops but was soon silenced by Bren guns on the boats.

FLIGHT SERGEANT
CHARLES COX

When we first visited Bruneval in the early 1960s we found it unspoiled. Although the villa itself had been destroyed in subsequent bombing (see page 36), the foundations remained. Also, back then, many of the participants on the raid were still alive, so we sent this photo to Major-General John Frost (as he then was) to ask him if he recognised this stairway as the one he used to enter the building. He replied that he thought it was.

We took this oblique shot of the area in April 1976 and R. V. Jones, then a Professor at the University of Aberdeen, added the annotations as he wanted to include it in his book and a television documentary on *The Secret War.*

When researching this raid for the feature in *After the Battle* No. 13, we tried everywhere to find copies of the photographs that were said to have been taken of the radar equipment on the raid. Drawing a blank, we asked Professor Jones and he said that 'so far as I know there was only one photograph taken, and it was by one of the Army officers and not by Cox himself. We never understood how it came about, but there were two photographs superimposed on one negative which was extremely difficult to get with a Leica which I understood was the camera used. The one photograph was of a hutted camp in England, presumably where the raiding party was stationed before the raid, and the other was a flashlight photograph of the inside of the Würzburg paraboloid, which had its claimed "kills" painted on it.'

In the battle at the Würzburg, Lieutenant Young's men had soon overrun the position, killing one defender. Of the remaining Germans, one ran the wrong way towards the cliff edge, 20 yards or so away. As he was chased by the paratroopers, he fell over the cliff but managed to save himself on a projecting rock. He was hauled to safety and taken prisoner.

With the Würzburg secured, Lieutenant Vernon scrambled up and examined it with a hand torch. Then, using a Leica, he began to photograph the aerial, an action no sooner made than regretted, since the blaze of light from the flashbulb attracted bullets from several directions. Vernon summoned the remainder of his team and ordered one sapper to saw off the aerial element while the remainder removed the components in the operating cabin. The aerial came away easily, but the main radar equipment defied several attempts to dismantle it with screwdrivers. This was no time for finesse as the bullets ricocheting from the cabin's walls were real enough. Crowbars were brought into play, and the radar set gave up the unequal struggle as the units were ripped out of the console.

Veterans of the 2nd Parachute Battalion revisited Bruneval in April 1976. Here they are inspecting the remains of the château.

Rifleman Hugh McIntyre was killed beside the Würzburg as the equipment was being loaded on trolleys.

Whilst the hand trolley, brought to transport the parts, was being loaded, Rifleman Hugh McIntyre was killed near the front door of the chateau. The firing was now increasing and Major Frost was concerned that if the Germans brought mortars into action, his force would be at a severe disadvantage.

He decided to settle for whatever the REs had dismantled and ordered the force to withdraw to the beach.

Heavy firing had been heard from the German beach defences to the south and when the party reached the crest of the hill, they were silhouetted against the skyline. The machine gun in the pill-box on the opposite hillside (code-named 'Beach Fort') directed its fire at them and wounded CSM Gerald Strachan. Whilst Major Frost dressed his wounds beside an unmanned pillbox (code-named 'Redoubt'), he heard Captain Ross call out that the beach had not yet been taken.

32

What had gone wrong? Of the party detailed to capture the beach, Lieutenant Charteris's men had landed three kilometres away near the hamlet of L'Enfer. Lieutenant Charteris could see from the following Whitleys, dropping their sticks further north, that they were south of Bruneval.

The Germans found the body of Private Alan Scott on the beach; apparently he had fallen to his death. Both the British casualties were buried by the Germans in Le Havre.

Six other men were missing when the force withdrew but they proved to have been captured. They all survived the war.

As they moved towards the sound of gun-fire in the moonlight, a German, thinking they were his own people, joined the line. He was silently killed but they had to shoot their way around Bruneval village, manned by a reserve platoon of Infanterie-Regiment 685. Lieutenant Charteris led the party at the double along the valley road towards the beach. Just as Major Frost was organising his own attack from the north with Lieutenant Naumoff's section, the missing paratroopers rushed forward shouting their war-cry. Attacked from two sides, the Germans abandoned the pillbox and disappeared. As they reached the house

on the beach, a villa called Stella Maris, they caught a German telephonist who was also quickly made prisoner.

Now it was a quarter past two. The beach was in British hands and on it were gathered the wounded, the German prisoners, and the pieces of equipment ripped from the Würzburg. Major Frost told his signallers to call in the naval assault craft to evacuate the force. On the cliffs on either side, the presence of German forces was becoming increasingly evident.

After a few minutes, the signallers reported that they had had no success in contacting the boats. As a last resort, two

green Very lights were fired. Then, as Frost later explained, 'with a sinking heart, I moved off the beach with my officers to rearrange our defences. It looked as though we were going to be left high and dry, and the thought was hard to bear.'

However, just as his troops began to take up positions for a final stand, Frost heard a cry: 'Sir, the boats are coming in. The boats are here! God bless the ruddy Navy, Sir!' Frost looked back and saw that six assault craft had slid to a stop on the beach. With a sigh of relief, he ordered his men to embark. From the boats themselves, covering fire was poured on to the Germans at the top of the cliffs.

February 28 at the Villa Orphée at Étretat. Private John Willoughby, Private Daniel Thomas and Lance-Corporal John

McCallum, all from the 'Nelson' group, are marched into captivity by Hauptmann Hubertus Prinz von Preussen.

At 0235 hours the force embarked. The German report on the raid stated that 'the operation of the British commandos was well planned and was executed with great daring. During the operation the British displayed exemplary discipline when under fire. Although attacked by German soldiers they concentrated entirely on their primary task. For a full 30 minutes one group did not fire a shot, then suddenly at the sound of a whistle they went into action.'

First on board were the men of the dismantling party carrying the precious pieces of equipment. Then came the prisoners and the wounded, and finally the rest of the paratroops. The landing craft backed away from the shore while the brisk exchange of fire continued until long after the boats were clear.

Safe aboard an assault craft, Major Frost learned the reason for the delay.

While he had actually been signalling, a German destroyer and two E-boats had passed within a mile of the small British flotilla. Fortunately they had not been noticed.

Mr Don Priest, a Telecommunications Research Establishment engineer, who had received a temporary commission as a flight lieutenant for the occasion, looked through the booty and Frost learned that the pieces of the radar set secured by his men were almost exactly what had been needed. (Had the coast been sufficiently clear, Priest would have landed to examine the actual Würzburg site first hand.)

As dawn broke, the returning assault craft were still only 15 miles from the French coast but an escort of several Spitfires arrived to escort the raiders back to England.

The only German casualties reported by the Abteilungskommandeur, Oberstleutnant Emil Terpe, were Obergefreiter Johannes Senge and Funker Paul Käfferbitz killed, and Unteroffizier Gerhard Wenzel and Obergefreiter Wilhelm Meseke wounded.

Surprisingly, Terpe only reported one man missing presumed captured so Funker Otto Heller must be one of those seen here. However, the Luftwaffe said they lost three men killed, with one man wounded and three missing.

GERMAN REPORT ON THE RAID

At 0055 hours on February 28, the Freya station reported aircraft north-north-east, range 29 kilometres.

The parachutists were sighted by the Army and the Luftwaffe ground and communications troops at 0115. The landing was made south-east of the farm [Le Presbytère] and was carried out in complete silence.

All Army and Luftwaffe posts in the area were at once alerted. Scouts sent from the Freya position (near Cap d'Antifer) and the Luftwaffe Communications Station [at Le Presbytère] returned with information that the enemy was on the move south of the farm in the direction of the château.

After the raid, the site at Bruneval was kept under close watch by the PRU squadrons, this sortie being carried out on Wednesday, August 12, 1942.

The parachutist commandos had split into several groups and were converging on the Würzburg position and on the château.

In La Poterie, the reserve platoon of the 1. Kompanie of Infanterie-Regiment 685 had just finished an exercise shortly after 0100 when the parachutists were sighted. The officer commanding at once made contact with the Bruneval Guard; the Sergeant there had already alerted his men.

The platoon reserve in Bruneval was ordered to occupy Hill 102 to the south-east of Bruneval. The officer command-

ing La Poterie platoon then led his men in a westerly direction towards the château.

On reaching the farm buildings north-east of the château the troops came under fire from the commando machine guns, and from the western end of the buildings they engaged the British who were already in possession of the Luftwaffe station [the Würzburg] near the farm. Here one of the commandos fell.

This German platoon encountered fire from the left flank, but the commandos were nevertheless prevented

Two shots from 1943: Wednesday, January 13 *(left)* **and Tuesday, April 13** *(right)*.

On the image:
LA POTERIE
BRUNEVAL
JUMEL
Light A.A.
Lighthouse
Semaphore Sta.
TARGET
ENGLISH CHANNEL

attacks through the ravine from seaward. The commandos, approaching from the north and north-east, were able to get close to these strongpoints under cover of the woods. Thus the German guard positions were attacked from the high ground by heavy fire from three or four commando machine guns. After one German soldier had been killed and another wounded the Sergeant was obliged to take up new positions. It was not until after one to one-and-a-half hours fighting that the commandos were able to get through the strongpoint and the ravine to the beach. With them the commandos took a wounded German soldier and also the soldier who had been on telephone watch at the post. Here another commando fell, and one was wounded. The latter was assisted to the boats, which had come close inshore on the exchange of signal flares.

The commandos embarked just as strong German reinforcements reached Bruneval.

The platoon from La Poterie fought their way to the Luftwaffe Communications Station [Würzburg] as the commandos withdrew. It was learned that the Luftwaffe personnel there had put up a stiff resistance, and only after some of them had exhausted their ammunition were the commandos able to break through to the Würzburg.

One of the crew had been killed by a British grenade as he tried to set off an explosive charge to destroy the Würzburg. The commandos then dismantled parts of the set and also took photographs. On conclusion of this task they obviously intended to attack the Freya station. The skilful intervention of the La Poterie platoon, however, prevented this.

When Medmenham were compiling the pre-D-Day list of radar stations, the one just to the north at Cap d'Antifer was the one mentioned in the German report of February, 1942. (See Target XII/31 on page 110.)

from proceeding with their attack on the Freya position. The remainder of the Luftwaffe Communications Station unit quartered in the farm buildings took part in this action.

In accordance with orders, the platoon from Bruneval village divided into two groups and advanced on Hill 102. Outside Bruneval they came under fire from the commandos who had landed north of L'Enfer.

Although this platoon was unable to prevent the commandos from infiltrating between Bruneval and Hill 102, it was because of this platoon's action that individual commandos did not reach the boats in time, and were later taken prisoner. One wounded commando was also captured. It was only because the British objective was not known that this Bruneval platoon did not take part in the action at the château.

The Bruneval Guard, one Sergeant and nine men, had meanwhile taken up prepared positions guarding the coast. These defensive positions were so built that they were effective only against

This shot taken on June 24, 1944 shows the whole area well and truly obliterated.

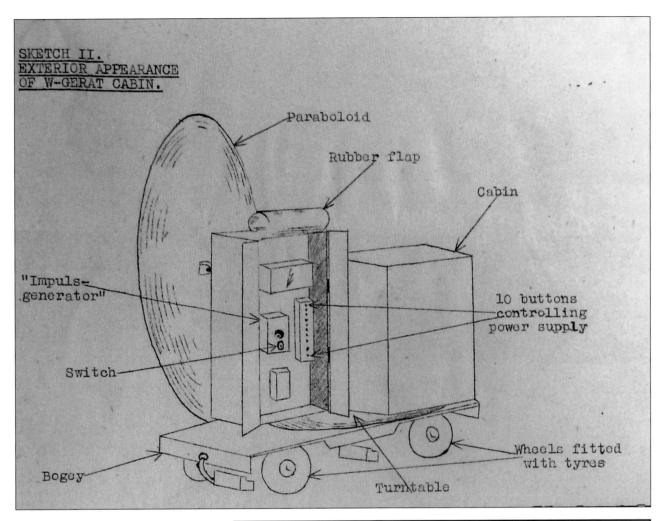

SKETCH II.
EXTERIOR APPEARANCE
OF W-GERÄT CABIN.

Paraboloid

Rubber flap

Cabin

"Impuls-
generator"

10 buttons
controlling
power supply

Switch

Wheels fitted
with tyres

Bogey

Turntable

Having made exhaustive enquiries to trace the whereabouts of the equipment brought back, none of the likely repositories — Royal Aircraft Establishment, Royal Signals and Radar Establishment, Imperial War Museum, etc, — could help us. In the end we asked Professor Jones and he said that the last time that he saw it was at the Telecommunications Research Establishment. He explained that 'when I arrived in my office the morning after the operation, a signal had already been received telling us of the successful execution of the raid, and that we could expect the captured equipment in the Air Ministry on the afternoon of Monday, 2nd March. The Bruneval booty was already in the Air Ministry, and it was obviously much better engineered than our own radar equipment, a fact which was readily admitted by our own radar men in their final report which included these drawings. Cox and his escort had done an excellent job. Only one important component had been left behind, an achievement all the more impressive because they had had only ten minutes at the Würzburg instead of the 30 which had been planned. Before the equipment went to TRE at Swanage for detailed examination, we took some of it out to the interrogation centre at Trent Park, Cockfosters, to discuss it with the operator who had been taken prisoner, and who was very co-operative. We were disappointed that despite his readiness to help, his technical competence was far lower than that of any of our own operators. In fact, up to that stage in the war, he had had more time in jail than out of it!'

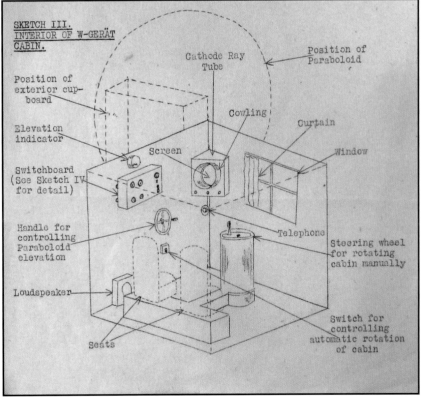

SKETCH III.
INTERIOR OF W-GERÄT
CABIN.

Cathode Ray
Tube

Position of
Paraboloid

Position of
exterior cup-
board

Cowling

Curtain

Elevation
indicator

Screen

Window

Switchboard
(See Sketch IV
for detail)

Handle for
controlling
Paraboloid
elevation

Telephone

Steering wheel
for rotating
cabin manually

Loudspeaker

Switch for
controlling
automatic rotation
of cabin

Seats

'We spent the afternoon sitting on the floor with him, fitting the various pieces together, and listening to his comments. On his last leave he had remarked to his wife that his station was so isolated that the English might easily make a raid and capture it.'

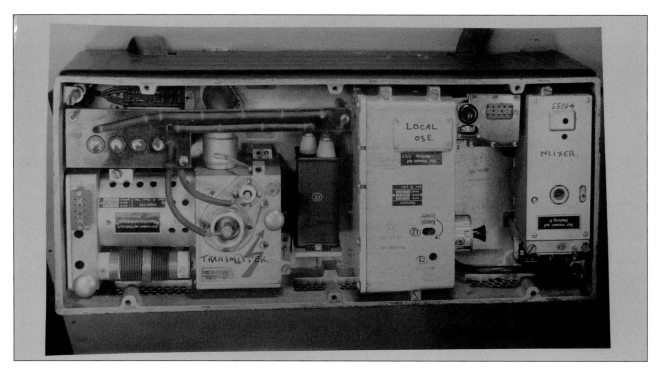

Interim Report on the Technical Results of the Raid on Bruneval on the 28th February, 1942.

Introduction

This report is necessarily brief because a complete investigation of the captured apparatus has not yet been finished. It is possible at this stage, however, to present some sort of picture of the results of the raid which although incomplete does indicate the degree of success achieved. A full report will be produced later. We will consider the state of technical knowledge of this branch of German RDF [Radio Direction Finding] before the raid and after it.

Although the items brought back have not survived, fortunately they were all photographed for the technical report. This is the front and back of the transmitter/receiver box.

The Position before the Raid

It was known that the GAF [German Air Force] possessed several types of RDF equipment working on a wavelength of 55cms, probably those referred to in the GAF as 'Wurzburg' and the position of one equipment in the Bruneval area was known exactly.

From the aerial photographs it was deduced that the Bruneval station contained an RDF equipment in addition to a 250cm. 'Freya' installation the details of which are fairly well known to us. It was presumed, but not certain, that this additional unit was a 55cm

equipment, controlling searchlights and AA fire, or was in general use on the Continent for this purpose.

The Objects of the Raid

(i) The success of the German AA and searchlight system had been somewhat disconcerting as we had lost many bombers. This success was most probably due to the RDF apparatus used for directing the fire. The primary object of the raid was therefore to obtain as much information as possible about this apparatus so that we could be in a position to take counter-measures.

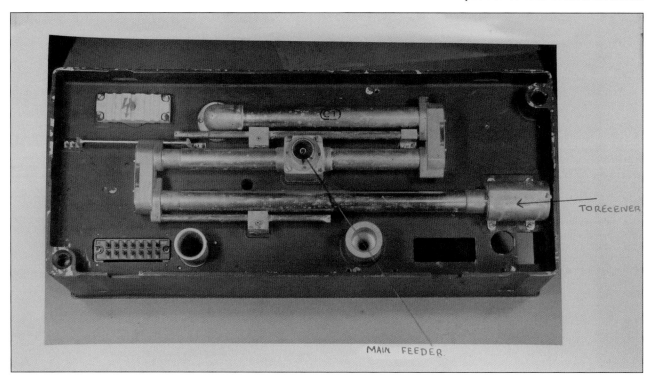

The modulator with the cathode ray tube removed.

(ii) Secondly, it was most desirable that we should be aware of the state of German RDF developments and technique on frequencies of the order of 600 Mc/s compared with our own.

(iii) Thirdly, experience in conducting combined operations of this nature, using paratroops, is greatly desired. This was the first paratroop raid since the one on Italy more than 12 months ago.

(iv) Fourthly, it was essential to our Air Intelligence that certain information about the German RDF system should be obtained as a check on the information received purely through Intelligence channels, most of which was incomplete.

The Results of the Raid including a brief description of the Captured Apparatus.

The major portion of the apparatus was carried away bodily. Owing to its excellent construction and the efficiency of the personnel who took it, it suffered very little damage and it has since been possible to make the separate units work in the laboratory at TRE [Telecommunications Research Establishment] without modification or reconstruction. The scale of effort necessary to make the apparatus completely operational will be largely compared with the small amount of addi-

tional knowledge that would be produced thereby and which is in any case provided by direct listening watch.

An operator was among those taken prisoner. Fortunately, he was very willing to impart information although his knowledge of the technical side of the equipment was very scanty. He has thrown a great deal of light on the

action of that portion of the apparatus which could not be brought back owing to lack of time, i.e. the presentation. He has also given us information about the organisation of personnel, the history of the station and the method of reporting.

The following description of the captured equipment will only be brief as the subject will be dealt with more fully in the main report to be published later.

The equipment consisted of a paraboloid about 30 feet in diameter with all the apparatus and the control cabin fixed on to the back, the whole unit being capable of rotation in azimuth by manual or motor control. The paraboloid could be rotated manually in the vertical plane. The whole unit was mounted on a trailer. The operator sat in the cabin.

Power was obtained from the French AC mains, giving about 175 volts at 50 cycles per second.

The equipment captured consisted of all that behind the paraboloid except the power supply, and the serial in front of it, and consisted of four pieces as follows:

The T/R Box

This is an aluminium box about 24½" × 10½" × 6¼" containing the common T and R feeder system, the transmitter unit, and the mixer and local oscillator units of the receiver.

The common T and R system does not make use of any spark gaps or devices to protect the mixer valve which is a double diode of robust construction. There is no amplification ahead of the diode.

The local oscillator, which is a highly stable one of unique construction using metal-coated ceramic material for the tuned circuits, consists of a tuned-plate tuned grid push-pull triode oscillator, probably on 200 cms driving a simple triode frequency quadrupler. The valves used are of particularly good construction and embody first class VHF technique. It is worth noting that there is no external tuning control on this unit and that all the tuning is done on the transmitter. The output is injected equally on to the anodes of the diode mixer capacitatively by means of a prong.

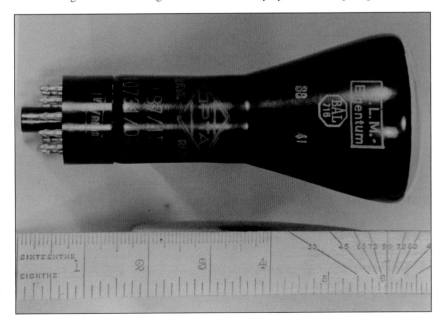

 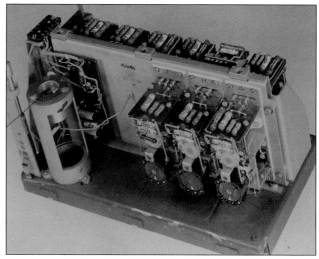

The front and back of the IF amplifier

It is interesting to note that this oscillator is contained in an iron box whereas everything else is aluminium. Also it is very much more elaborate than is required for this purpose. It is very likely therefore that it is common to other German equipment — probably the communication equipment which is known to exist on wavelengths of about 50 cms.

The transmitter is a single valve Colpitts oscillator using a negative grid triode, the pulse modulation applied to the grid. The peak power output is estimated as 5 kilowatts, approximately. The load is taken from a resonant circuit inductively coupled to the main tank circuit which is linear and has a variable ceramic condenser between the low-voltage ends of the grid and anode lines. The anode feed circuit incorporates a long time constant probably to reduce the bad effects of accidental CW operation.

The Impulse Generator Unit
This is in a box measuring 13" × 12¾" × 6¾" and contains 10 Telefunken LS 50 pentodes in a straightforward circuit rather similar to our own CHL modulator circuit. No trigger circuits are used, hence the large number of valves. A black-out pulse is also produced. The unit incorporates small CRT for monitoring, very similar to one of our own types. A relay enables the pulse width to be varied from one to two microseconds, approximately.

The Receiver IF Amplifier
This is in a box 6½" × 7" × 12½". There are four stages of amplification at 24 Mc/s approximately, followed by a second oscillator at 19 Mc/s and mixer, and three stages on 6 Mc/s, approximately. There are evidently some more amplifying stages which are missing, presumably in the presentation equipment. Band width is about 0.5 Mc/s.

The aerial in the centre of the parabola was an important item needed for examination and in the end it just had to be wrenched off by brute force. (Aviation historian Andy Saunders was given some of the Würzburg equipment when Farnborough was disposing of unwanted items but said that he moved them on in later years.)

The Aerial System
The actual paraboloid was left behind but the rest was taken. This consists of a single dipole and a periodic reflector of curious design, probably to give a wide frequency band characteristic. These are mounted on the end of a horizontal aluminium support enclosing the single concentric feeders and balance to unbalance transformer. The polarisation is vertical. There is no split; the D/F is done by working on the maximum of the beam.

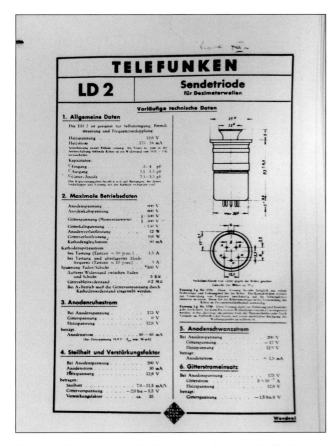

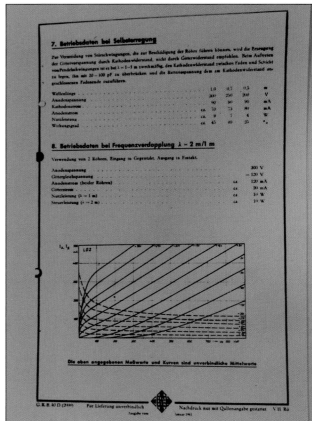

All the radar equipment had been manufactured by Telefunken and was considered to be very well constructed with great use being made of aluminium, sand and die castings. All the radio parts were in unit form for easy maintenance and/or replacement.

Any alteration of frequency at all would have to be done by a skilled technician and would take time.

Further it could not be moved outside the limits of 53 cms and 56.5 cms (a coverage of 36 Mc/s). The limit is set by the transmitter unit.

By the substitution of new units, however, it would be possible to extend the frequency range considerably further than this, between limits not at present calculated accurately but probably of the order of 45 cms to 60 cms.

These figures may be modified by the addition of a split unit to give more accurate D/F such as almost certainly exists on some other stations. A further estimate of this will be made in the main report.

As far as is known, no anti-jamming devices exist on this particular equipment and the presentation consisted of a circular time-base of 30km circumference with the signals radiating outwards from the circle. A small tube was used, probably about 4 inches in diameter.

From this captured apparatus and information, the following facts emerge:

(i) The apparatus does work on 53 cms.
(ii) It is known as 'Wurzburg'.
(ii) Technically it is fairly elementary and reveals no ideas or methods that were not previously known in this country, although it is known from listening evidence that the equipment captured is not the latest German design.

(iv) This particular equipment is so elementary that it could not possibly be used for controlling AA fire sufficiently accurately to account for our bomber losses. This is because the D/F accuracy is not good enough.

(v) Its method of construction, however, in easily replaceable units, shows that it would be possible by replacing some of the units to modify it and incorporate in it features that are known to exist in the latest designs. The addition of these features with certain others would make accurate AA fire control feasible.

(vi) Valuable information has been obtained from the apparatus which indicates the possible range of frequency that could be obtained by adjustments. This information is of the greatest importance to our jamming effort.

(vii) Other details which would have been useful from the jamming viewpoint were unfortunately not revealed because they were contained in that portion of the gear that was left behind. We have found out something about the range of frequency over which the gear is adjustable, (a) on site and (b) by fitting new units sent from a maintenance base. This is of paramount importance since it provides the data which is unobtainable in any other way, on which the design of comprehensive jamming equipment can be based.

Evidence obtained by TRE Enemy Investigation Group

Before the value of the above results can be assessed, the contributory evidence obtained from 'listening services' has to be added. Summarised this evidence is as follows:

(i) Before about the middle of February 1942, it was quite clear from the results obtained by these investigations that nearly all the 53cm stations under observation round the Continental coast were unsuitable for AA fire control since they were not fitted with accurate D/F.

(ii) Since then, as time has gone on, more and more of these stations have been modified to include the features giving sufficiently accurate D/F for AA fire control and the maximum ranges have been increased as is indicated by reduced repetition frequencies. Whether this has been done by installing completely new apparatus or by modifying the earlier apparatus was not known, but the circumstantial evidence would be in accordance with gradual modification. Examination of the captured equipment shows that such modifications are feasible.

(iii) Very recently, enemy transmissions on a frequency of 470 Mc/s (a wavelength of 64 cms) have been observed.

Major-General John Frost: 'The first occasion that I returned to Bruneval was in March 1947 for the unveiling of a memorial by Général de Gaulle. There was a terrible traffic mix-up that forced many of the VIPs to foot it across country, among them the British Ambassador and Lady Diana Duff Cooper. I never managed to meet the Général who ignored the Parachute Regiment Guard of Honour and made no reference in his speech to the part that we British had played, but I believe it was all a great success from a political point of view as it initiated the formation of the Rassemblement du Peuple Français.'

It was fitting that a memorial plaque had been placed on 'Beach Fort' pillbox. We photographed the view as it appeared in 1961.

In 1975, another plaque was unveiled at the pillbox by Admiral of the Fleet, The Earl Mountbatten of Burma, seen here with General Frost.

General Frost explained in his narrative *A Drop Too Many* published in 1980 that 'on another occasion, Headquarters Combined Operations sponsored a return and some of us went over in great comfort aboard Royal Navy destroyers. Members of 44 Parachute Brigade of the Territorial Army parachuted in very adverse weather so they came down oscillating most alarmingly, breaking telephone lines and the roof of an ambulance in the process. Nevertheless, no one was really hurt and a young naval officer was heard to say: "We shall have to revise our ideas about pongos after this".' *Above:* In 1975 a huge new memorial, designed by Bruno Saas, with a 'Charles de Gaulle Staircase', was proposed which was inaugurated on June 24, 2012 by Kenneth Holden *(right)*, a gunner on *MGB 317*, the last surviving participant of the operation.

Construction of the new memorial involved cutting away part of the hillside so destroying the uniqueness of the original location of 'Beach Fort' pillbox from which fire was brought down on the raiding party as it moved down to the beach.

Bruneval was the first battle honour earned by the Parachute Regiment and C (Bruneval) Company of the 2nd Battalion, under Major Al Hortop, visited Bruneval on the 75th anniversary of the raid.

Members of 2 Para walked in the footsteps of their forebears from the drop zone to the target and then down the hillside to the beach. They then formed up in remembrance at the memorial.

One wonders if a thought was spared for the airman whose daring exploit 75 years before was the catalyst for launching Operation 'Biting'. Squadron Leader Tony Hill, whose photographs started the chain of events that led to the raid, later commanded No. 543 Squadron and was shot down on October 18, 1942 during a low-level photographic mission to Le Creusot in south-eastern France. He broke his back in the crash but was rescued by the French Resistance. An aircraft was laid on to fly him back to England but he died as he was being carried to the plane on November 12. He now lies buried in Les Péjoces Communal Cemetery in Dijon. The inscription on his headstone reads: 'He that loseth his life for my sake shall find it'.

From 1936 to 1939 Reginald Jones was Scientific Officer at the Air Ministry, becoming MI6's principal scientific adviser when war began. In 1941 he was appointed Assistant Director of Intelligence (Science), and was heavily involved with the scientific assessment of enemy technology. His remit was wide-ranging and he was cleared to receive top secret Enigma messages that had been decoded by the deciphering service at Bletchley Park. Jones achieved success in countering the Luftwaffe's navigational beam guidance system and, as radar was his main speciality, he briefed Flight Sergeant Cox before the raid on Bruneval. He also developed the method of blinding German radar with strips of metal foil called 'Window' and, as he explains here in this foreword, it was due to his efforts that the 'Rhubarb' target folders came about. Professor Jones, as he later became at Aberdeen University, was also at the forefront of introducing measures to help combat the V-weapon campaign. He died in December 1997.

Operations Against Coastal Radar Stations

By R. V. Jones

At the same time as we were watching the flying bomb trials, dealing with the Baby Blitz, and wrestling with the German night defences, another problem was approaching its climax: this was the coming operation to land in force in Normandy. Ever since 1940 I had known what my part must be, whether or not it was formally assigned to me: to see that everything possible was done to knock out, by jamming, deception, or direct action, the chain of coastal radar stations that the Germans would inevitably build up. This had been my answer in 1941 to the physicist A. P. 'Jimmy' Rowe, the Chief Superintendent of the Telecommunications Research Establishment (TRE), when he asked me what good it was my collecting detailed Intelligence on all German radar stations. I had replied that some time we were going back and those stations might stand between our success and failure.

In general, by the end of 1943 we knew enough about the various forms of coastal radar to jam much of the system successfully, and to organise deceptions by using 'Window' to simulate large forces at sea as well as in the air. But if we could make direct attacks on German radar stations, some of them could be eliminated, and the operators in the others might be so disturbed as to observe less accurately in the presence of jamming. From the beginning, therefore, I had advocated direct attack.

Fighter Command at first said that it could not carry out attacks on such small targets as radar stations because fighters could not find them. I therefore suggested that each fighter squadron should be led by a photo-reconnaissance pilot, and this suggestion may have shamed the Command into improving its low-level navigation. Anyway, by the beginning of 1944 there was serious consideration of using fighter squadrons against the radar stations in the invasion area.

The work of building up the information about the positions and types of German radar equipment on the coast was shared between my unit and Claude Wavell's in the Central Interpretation Unit at Medmenham, and over the years we had jointly produced a series of dossiers for what were known as 'Rhubarb' operations, these being the general title of any offensive actions by Fighter Command over France and the Low Countries. To the general operational instructions there was a series of appendices, and ours was Appendix XII, of which we produced several editions as the intensity of German radar cover increased. The result was that, although we never had an operational requirement stated to us, there was a comprehensive dossier on every German coastal radar station, including maps, and high- and low-level photographs, in sufficient detail for accurate attacks to be planned.

Moreover, we produced recognition drawings of all known types of German radar equipment, and catalogues of all the radar stations between Skagen at the northern tip of Denmark, and Bayonne on the west of France near the Spanish frontier. Even though we knew that our attack was to be made in Normandy, we covered a very much wider coastline, so that if any leakage of information were to occur, the Germans would have no clue regarding the selected area. Our catalogue listed nearly 200 separate stations which between them contained some 600 individual radar installations.

We were now producing many copies of our reports—more than 300 of each were circulated to headquarters and field units, both British and American, and we supplied the information for all three Services of both nations. In this, we had the enthusiastic support, particularly, of the United States Navy, even though as late as

March 1944, I still had no formal request for information on German radar, nor was I formally brought into the invasion planning. At last, an officer who had been on the first course to which I had lectured at the RAF Staff College, came in to consult me, since he had officially been assigned to the problem of knocking out the German radar. But it was clear that his scale of operations would be much too small to be effective. I was therefore wondering how I could intervene, when I had to give a further lecture at the Staff College on April 13, 1944. When I arrived there, Air Vice-Marshal Charles Medhurst, the College commandant, told me that Sir Arthur Tedder, the Deputy Supreme Allied Commander, would be giving the lecture after mine, and Medhurst wondered whether I would care to listen to him before we all went to lunch. I told Medhurst that Tedder was just the man I wanted to see, because of the inadequate planning of countermeasures against German radar, and that I would like a chance to talk with him. Medhurst, once again delighted to be able to 'fix' something, told me that he would see if he could arrange for a quiet half-hour between me and Tedder after lunch.

He left the two of us in his room, and I told the Deputy Supreme Commander why I thought that the plans were inadequate. He was quickly convinced and asked me what he should do — after all, the invasion was less than two months away. I told him that he should send a request to the Air Staff for as high level a party as possible to be formed at the headquarters of the Allied Expeditionary Air Force, nominating Victor Tait, the Director General of Signals, to head the party. Then, almost certainly, Victor Tait would ask me to join him to provide the Intelligence, and I could then bring in those members of my staff who would best be able to help.

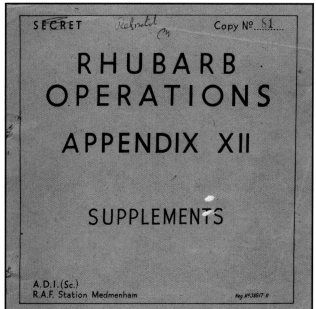

The file produced by the Central Interpretation Unit was marked 'SECRET' and was distributed to concerned formations in March 1944. Main recipients were Air Defence Great Britain (formerly RAF Fighter Command); the Second Tactical Air Force; USAAF VIII Fighter Command, and the US Ninth Air Force. File copies were also given to the Admiralty and War Office. A supplement, covering new stations detected, was issued that May. (The term 'Rhubarb' was used to describe offensive operations by fighters designed to make the enemy retain strong air forces in Western Europe.) The report explains that 'the target sites are dealt with individually in topographical order, starting at the Franco-Belgian frontier. The description gives the co-ordinates of the target but since most are within a short distance of the sea coast, and involve little flying over land, it is not usually necessary to give information on the best line of approach. Known Flak positions are annotated but it must be remembered that only those can be included which are known at the date of issue of the Appendix. Whenever available, vertical photographs of different scales as well as low obliques are included. A line plan, generally to a scale of 100 feet to one inch, shows the layout of the target itself together with ancillary buildings. Successful attack will inevitably embarrass the enemy, though his reaction is likely to be speedy. Damage to the aerial system will probably deprive him of his plots for at least half a day. Furthermore, it is German practice to have a single repair party to cover a number of stations, the station personnel only being trained to perform routine maintenance such as changing valves. So a concentrated attack would certainly leave the enemy with a proportion of sets unserviceable for a longer period.'

Medhurst wrote to me later that same afternoon saying, 'I hope that your talk with Tedder will bear fruit!' It evidently did, for a few days later Tait rang me up to tell me that he did not know how it had come about but there had been a request from Supreme Headquarters for him to organise a party at Allied Expeditionary Air Force (AEAF) to run the counter-measures against the German radar stations, and that he would like me to join him and do all the Intelligence work. We quickly formed our party, and started on a much enlarged plan of attack.

One of my first steps was to visit Supreme Headquarters in Bushey Park to make contact with some of the Planning Staff. Among them was Major Manus, a Canadian, who exclaimed: 'Dr. Jones? Good God! I thought that you were dead!' When I asked him why, he replied, 'I gave orders for you to be shot!' It turned out that he had previously been on the Planning Staff for the Dieppe raid, and he had understood that I myself was going on the raid. He had therefore detailed two men to guard me as far as possible but had also ordered them to shoot me if I were about to be captured by the Germans, because with my knowledge I was such a security risk. He told me that he had not been on the raid himself, but that he had been waiting to meet the survivors as they landed and could find no trace of me, and he therefore thought it best not to make any further enquiries.

This is the explanation underlying James Leasor's book *Green Beach,* and also a legal action fought by Quentin Reynolds about someone going on the Dieppe raid who was to be shot if in danger of capture.

Green Beach is the story of Flight Sergeant Jack Nissenthal, who in fact did go on the Dieppe raid as the expert ready to dismantle the German radar station at Pourville if it was captured during the raid. This was in August 1942, some months after Bruneval, but it differed from the latter in being a very much larger raid, and the radar was only a subsidiary target instead of being the main one. There was a suggestion that Flight Sergeant Cox should again go on the Dieppe raid, but I advised him that I thought that he had already 'done his bit', and so another Flight Sergeant was selected from the volunteers. This was Nissenthal and somehow the order that would have applied to me had I gone on the raid (and I have heard a story that there was a similar order regarding Don Priest, had he landed at Bruneval) was transferred to him. Actually there was no more reason for him to be shot than there would have been for Cox in the Bruneval Raid, since they knew comparable amounts about our own radar, and only as much about German radar as was necessary for dismantling captured equipment. It was the misapprehension of Major Manus regarding my own presence on the raid that resulted in his dramatic order.

For D-Day, it was important to know how much effort we should need to knock out a major radar installation, and so we decided to have a trial attack on one of the largest types of German equipment, known to us as a 'Chimney', because of the appearance of the large supporting column which held the array, and to the Germans as 'Wassermann 3'. It was rather like a Hoarding turned with its long side vertical and mounted on a swivelling column, and had the advantage that it could determine height as well as range. I decided on a 'Chimney' near Ostend, because our Belgian espionage network was excellent, and we briefed our agents about the date and time of attack so that they could observe its effects.

I decided on a Chimney' near Ostend, because our Belgian espionage network was excellent and we briefed our agents about the date and time of attack so that they could observe its effects. The attack took place on March 16 with rocket-firing Typhoons of No. 198 Squadron, and was very succcessful.

As regards the tactics of the campaign, it would clearly be dangerous to attack only the radar stations that could cover our intended landing area, and so we had a general rule that for every one attack that we made in the area there should be two outside it, so that the Germans should not be able to deduce from the intensity of our pre-invasion attacks exactly where the landings were to be made.

[1] Ypres/Voormezele
[2] Dunkirk/Fort des Dunes
[3] Gravelines/Le Clipon
[4] Gravelines/Petit-Fort-Philippe
[5] Cap Blanc-Nez
[6] Cap Blanc-Nez/St Pol
[7] Cap Gris-Nez
[8] Cap Gris-Nez/Pointe du Riden
[9] Cap Gris-Nez/Bellevue
[10] Cap Gris-Nez/Wattermel St
    George
[11] Cap Gris-Nez/Onglevert
[12] Boulogne/Boursin
[13] Boulogne/Monument
[14] Boulogne/Mont Lambert
[15A] Boulogne/Cap d'Alprech
[15B] Boulogne/Cap d'Alprech
[16] Boulogne/Hardelot
[17] Mont Violette
[18] Neufchâtel/Mont St Frieux
[19] Le Touquet/Plage Ste Cécile
[20] Fruges/Prédefin
[21] Aubigny/Frévillers
[22] Berck-sur-Mer
[23] Cayeux/Nouveau Brighton
[24] Amiens/Montrelet
[25] Abbeville/Vaudricourt
[26] Le Tréport/Mont Huon
[27] Dieppe/Caude-Côte
[28] St Valéry-en-Caux/
    Manneville ès Plains
[29] St Valéry-en-Caux/
    St Martin-aux-Buneaux
[30] Fécamp/Chapelle de la Vierge
[31] Cap d'Antifer/Sémaphore
[32] Cap d'Antifer
[33] Yvetot/Épinay-sur-Duclair
[34] Neufchâtel/Sully
[35] Le Havre/Cap de la Hève
[36] Lisieux/Le Theil-Nolent
[37] Bernay/La Chalière
[38] Houlgate/Sémaphore
[39] Caen/Douvres-la-Délivrande
[40] Arromanches
[41] Pointe et Raz de la Percée
[42] St Lô/Bourg d'Enfer
[43] Vire/Le Parc
[44] Barfleur/Le Vicel
[45] Cherbourg/Cap Lévy
[46] Cherbourg/Fermanville (La
    Brasserie)
[47] Omonville la Rogue/Asselins
[48] Cap de la Hague/Auderville
[49] Cap de la Hague/Jobourg
[50] Cap de Carteret/Sémaphore
[51] Guernsey/Fort George
[52] Guernsey/Pleinemont
[53] Jersey/Rouge Nez
[54] St Malo/Pointe du Grouin
[55] Cap Fréhel/Sémaphore
[56] Moncontour/Bel-Air
[57] Loudéac/La Récompense
[58] Monterfil/Les Épinais
[59] Vitré/La Haye
[60] Oisseau/Marêtre
[61] Falaise/Ri
[62] Dieppe/Ste Marguerite
[63] St Valéry-en-Caux/St Leger
[64] Bayeux/Le Mesnil
[65] Calais/Sangatte.

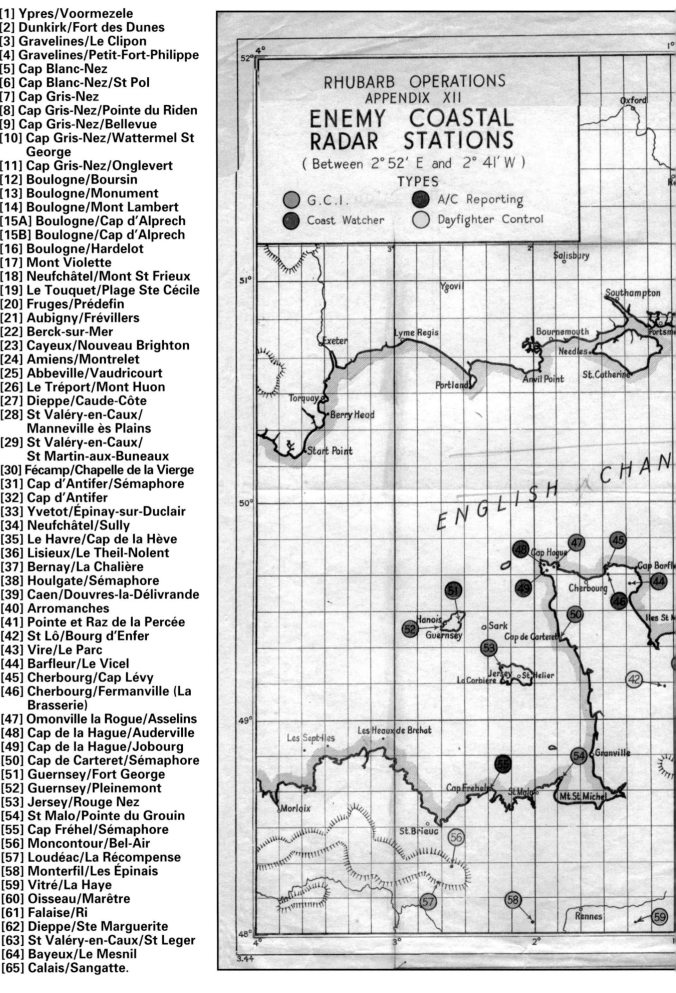

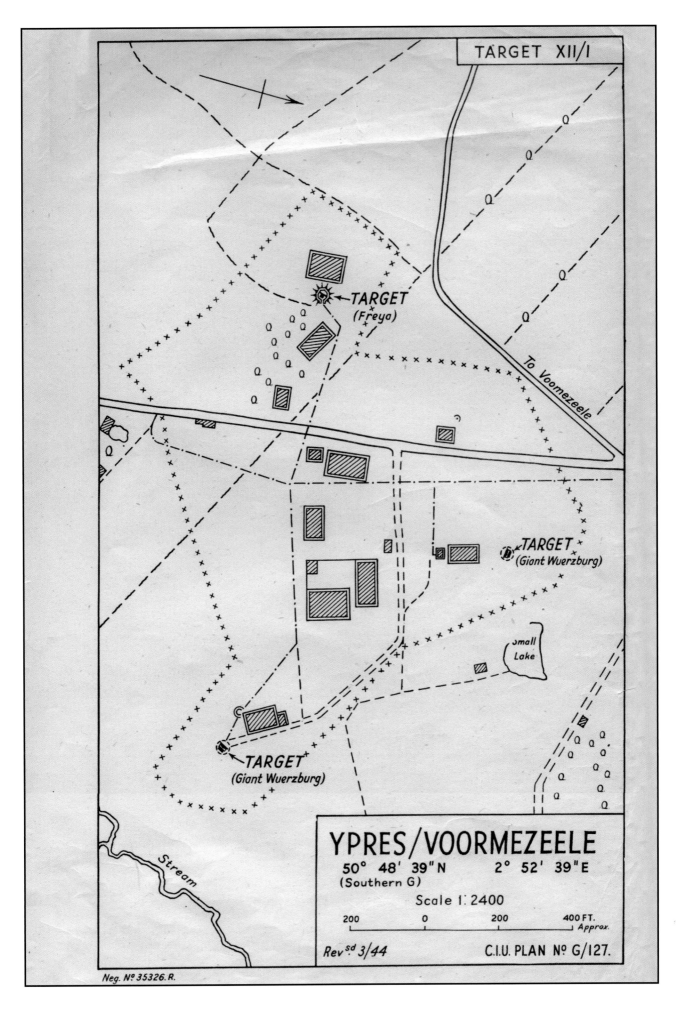

TARGET XII/1

→ TARGET
  (Freya)

To Voormezeele

TARGET
(Giant Wuerzburg)

Small
Lake

← TARGET
  (Giant Wuerzburg)

Stream

YPRES/VOORMEZEELE
50° 48′ 39″N   2° 52′ 39″E
(Southern G)

Scale 1: 2400

200   0   200   400 FT.
                                    Approx.

Rev^sd 3/44   C.I.U. PLAN N° G/127.

Neg. N° 35326.R.

51

DUNKIRK/FORT DES DUNES

Target XII/2 was located in a 19th century French fortification which backed on to the dunes three miles east of Dunkirk. Its German code-name was 'Dahlie'.

COASTAL SHIP-WATCHING STATION

Co-ordinates: 51° 03'15"N 2° 26' 52" E
Grid reference: 296857
Altitude: 20ft

This coastal station is sited on the northern ramparts of the Fort des Dunes, an old fort about ½ mile inland from the sea-front at Zuydcoote, and approximately three miles east-north-east of Dunkirk.

The target consists of a single Giant Würzburg.

Defence positions exist at the fort and these do not appear to have been added to.

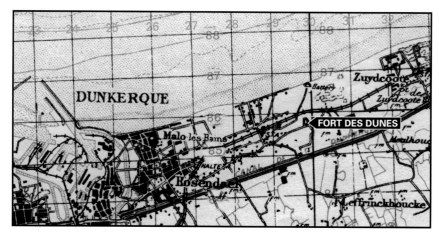

Originally known as the Fort de l'Est, it was built between 1878 and 1880 at the same time as the Zuydcoote Battery some distance to the north, to protect Dunkirk and its port from attacks from the east. Part of the Séré de Rivières system, it was armed with a variety of weaponry and manned by a garrison of 450 men. Being far behind the lines, it saw no action during the 1914-1918 war but it was a different story in the Second World War. On June 2, 1940, the Luftwaffe bombed the fort where the headquarters of the 12ème Division d'Infanterie Motorisée was then established, killing Général Louis Janssen, the commander of the division, and several of his staff. Another aerial attack on June 3 caused more deaths and damage, bringing the total losses to artillery and aerial bombing to over 150. The northern part of the fort, with the hexagonal base for the Würzburg Giant radar is visible top right.

CANAL DES DUNES

FORT DES DUNES

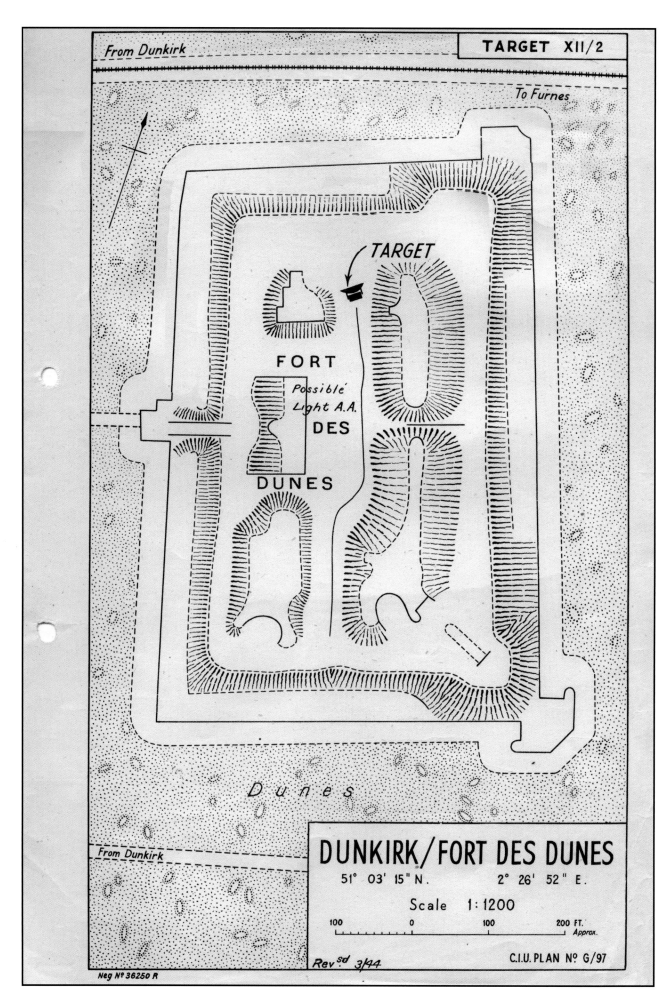

As soon as the last evacuations had taken place from the Dunkirk beaches and port on June 4, the Germans took possession. Once the access bridge broken by a Stuka bomb had been repaired, the fort became an annex to the nearby Zuydcoote Battery. The Germans set up a theatre in the old powder magazine in the Fort des Dunes, and the wooden stage they built is still visible today, as well as a nice fresco inspired by the famous movie *Metropolis*. *Right:* Another highlights of the visits is the concrete base of the Giant Würzburg.

On September 4, 1944, one young member of the Resistance attempted to intercept a lone German soldier in nearby Rosendaël, seemingly to capture his rifle. The attempt failed but the Germans quickly traced the house where the assailant escaped. They assaulted the house and arrested eight men hiding there, one of them being wounded by a grenade during the operation. They were first taken to the Zuydcoote Battery where one of them, Daniel Decroos, was killed when he tried to escape. The seven men were then taken to the fort to be executed on September 6 in the northern ditch. The wounded man was also put to death. The Dunkirk Pocket held out until the final surrender in May 1945. In the summer, wrecks of collapsed masonry were searched in the northern ditch to recover the remains of the executed men and after a ceremony on August 6, 1945, they were re-interred in various family graves. Later more excavations were carried out to trace the remains of those who had been killed in the bombing in 1940 and all were re-interred in a military cemetery just north of the fort entrance; the cemetery now comprises 190 graves. Bought in 1998 by the commune of Leffrinckoucke the fort was cleared and restored and open to visits from 2010. The Fort des Dunes is now open to visits from February to November.

GRAVELINES/LE CLIPON

AIRCRAFT REPORTING STATION

Co-ordinates: 51° 01' 34"N 2° 12' 25"E
Grid reference: 125839
Altitude: 20ft

Situated on a high point in the dunes between Gravelines and Dunkirk, on the seaward side of the minor road from Gravelines to Le Clipon. Mardick airfield lies less than two miles the east.

The radar station is manned by elements of the Marine-Artillerie-Abteilung 204.

Target XII/3 lay some six miles down the coast from Dunkirk at Gravelines. Today the town is better known as the site of the largest nuclear power station in western Europe. This is made up of six reactors, each producing 900 megawatts, which equates to more than eight per cent of the whole of the electricity produced in France. The cooling water is discharged into the English Channel.

The target consists of two Giant Würzburgs, one small Würzburg and two Pole-type Freya apparatuses. The Giants lie 425 yards apart on a bearing of 244½° true, the more westerly standing on one of the highest spots in the dunes. One of the Freya apparatuses is situated alongside the coastal road midway between the Giants; the other is north-west of the more westerly Giant. The small Würzburg is situated 100 yards north-east of the eastern Giant.

The site is enclosed by a defence trench partly covered with camouflage and two belts of wire, one conforming roughly to the plan of the trench.

Station buildings are still under construction, notably a large building east of the easterly Freya. Further camouflage work and the cutting of defence trenches is also in progress. The photo was taken on October 20, 1943.

The site of the Gravelines/Le Clipon radar has been totally lost with the post-war construction of the Canal des Dunes.

Loon Plage Motorcross Circuit and a nearby shooting range now occupy the area.

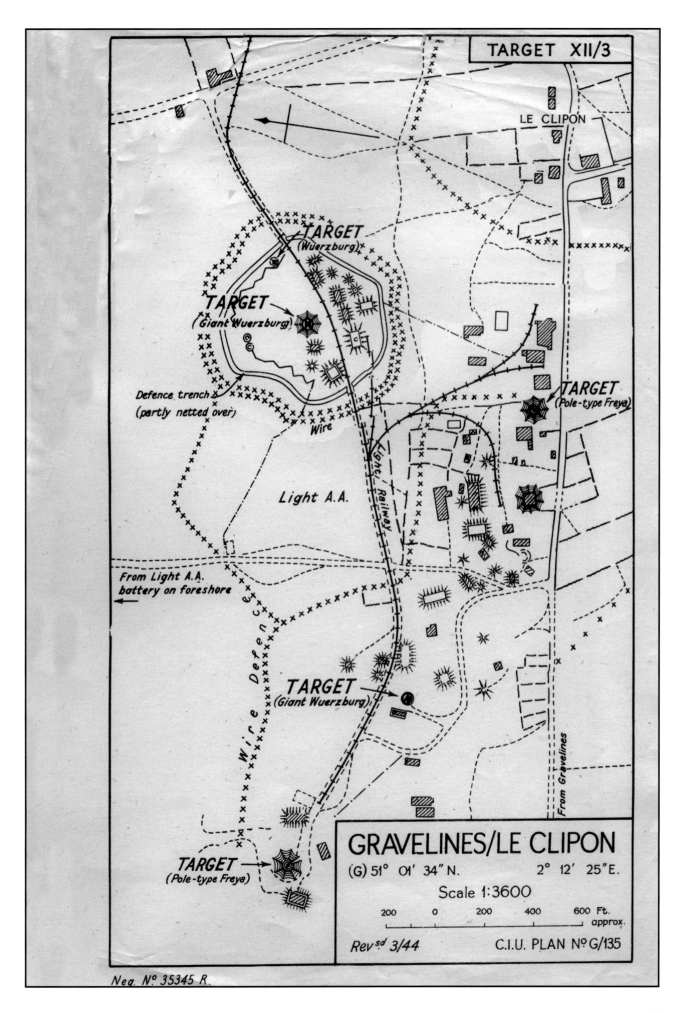

TARGET XII/3

LE CLIPON

TARGET
(Wuerzburg)

TARGET
(Giant Wuerzburg)

c

Defence trench
(partly netted over)

Wire

TARGET
(Pole-type Freya)

Light A.A.

Light Railway

From Light A.A.
battery on foreshore

Wire Defence

TARGET
(Giant Wuerzburg)

From Gravelines

TARGET
(Pole-type Freya)

GRAVELINES/LE CLIPON
(G) 51° 01′ 34″ N.   2° 12′ 25″ E.
Scale 1:3600

200   0   200   400   600 Ft.
                                                  approx.

Rev^sd 3/44   C.I.U. PLAN N° G/135

Neg. N° 35345 R.

GRAVELINES/PETIT-FORT-PHILIPPE

COASTAL SHIP-WATCHING STATION

Co-ordinates: 51° 00'37"N 2° 07' 24"E
Grid reference: 065826
Altitude: 20ft

Situated on a high point on the seaward edge of the dunes ¾ mile from Petit-Fort-Philippe on the eastern side of the canal connecting Gravelines with the North Sea. The position is about 1½

Another radar site located in the dunes lay a short distance to the west. This was Target XII/4 on the Medmenham list.

miles due north of Gravelines, and directly in front of a large farm building. The German code-name was 'Krimhild' and it was operated by the 2. Marine-Funk-Mess-Abteilung.

The nuclear power station has now been pixelated on the latest Google Earth so this clear image is from 2004.

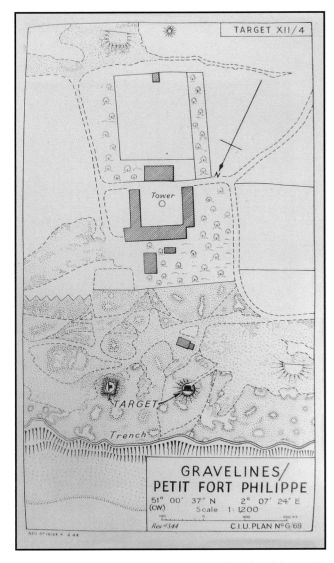

TARGET XII/4

Tower

TARGET

Trench

GRAVELINES/
PETIT FORT PHILIPPE

51° 00' 37" N   2° 07' 24" E
(CW)   Scale 1:1,200

Rev ³344   C.I.U. PLAN N° G/69

As most attacks would be mounted at low level from the seaward side, the target plans produced by the Central Interpretation Unit are usually presented to help the pilot identify the site on his approach from that direction. Hence north is not necessarily at the top like all conventional mapping.

This comparison looks in the same direction but little remains to be seen today in the scrubland behind the beach. The prominent building, originally from a farm known as the Ferme Decaestecker, was a cultural centre for 20 years, concerts being given there, before it closed in 2018.

The target consists of one Coastwatcher and one Giant Würzburg. The Coastwatcher stands in a square concrete emplacement of which two opposite corners are covered over. The Giant occupies a circular concrete emplacement some yards west of the Coastwatcher.

Considerable constructional activity is in progress at and near the site, which may be in connection with defence works.

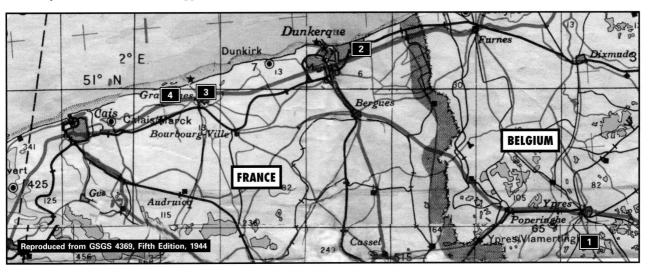

Reproduced from GSGS 4369, Fifth Edition, 1944

[1] Ypres/Voormezeele. [2] Dunkirk/Fort des Dunes. [3] Gravelines/Le Clipon. [4] Gravelines/Petit-Fort-Philippe.

CAP BLANC-NEZ

AIRCRAFT REPORTING STATION

Co-ordinates: 50° 55' 47"N 1° 42' 52"E
Grid reference: 772759
Altitude: 300ft

On the seaward slopes on and to the north-east of Cap Blanc-Nez, between the Monument, a tall obelisk, and the edge of the cliffs.

The target consists of two Giant Würzburgs and one Freya apparatus. The first of the Giants is installed on a circular concrete base at the top of the

In July 1914, the Dover Patrol was formed to cover the southern portion of the North Sea and the eastern part of the English Channel, including the Straits of Dover. Its duties included escorts for merchant ships, hospital ships and those transporting troops; anti-submarine patrols; sweeping for German mines and laying British minefields, and attacking German land forces along the coastline of France and Belgium. One of the most well-known actions was the blocking of the entrance to the port of Zeebrugge on April 22-23, 1918, an operation that led to the award of six Victoria Crosses. To commemorate the 2,000 members of the patrol who had lost their lives during the war, a monument 75 feet high, designed by Sir Aston Webb, was erected near Dover in 1921 *(left)* and a similar obelisk unveiled the following year on the cliff-top at Cap Blanc-Nez *(right)*.

cliffs 60 yards in front of the monument. Close to the monument, and forming a conspicuous feature, is a building surrounded by a cluster of 14 masts supporting dipole aerials. The second Giant is about 600 yards further along the cliffs to the north-east. The Freya

apparatus is in a square emplacement 60 yards south-west of the second Giant. Near it is a similar emplacement containing another apparatus of about the same height but of different design.

The whole area is heavily defended by mines, wire and trenches.

Today, Target XII/5 at Cap Blanc-Nez is littered with the remnants of the German fortifications which comprised the Atlantic Wall.

The Germans gave the site the code-word 'Düsseldorf' — the base of one of the Würzburgs still remains to be seen.

Monument
Radio masts surrounding building
TARGET (the more Westerly "Giant Wuerzburg")

View looking South

At some point the Germans pulled down the conspicuous memorial as it lay close to the radar site although it was still standing when these pictures were taken in July 1943.

Possibly it was the close attention of RAF photo-reconnaissance aircraft that prompted the demolition. The monument was rebuilt in 1962.

Observatory
Site of the most Easterly TARGET ("Giant Wuerzburg")

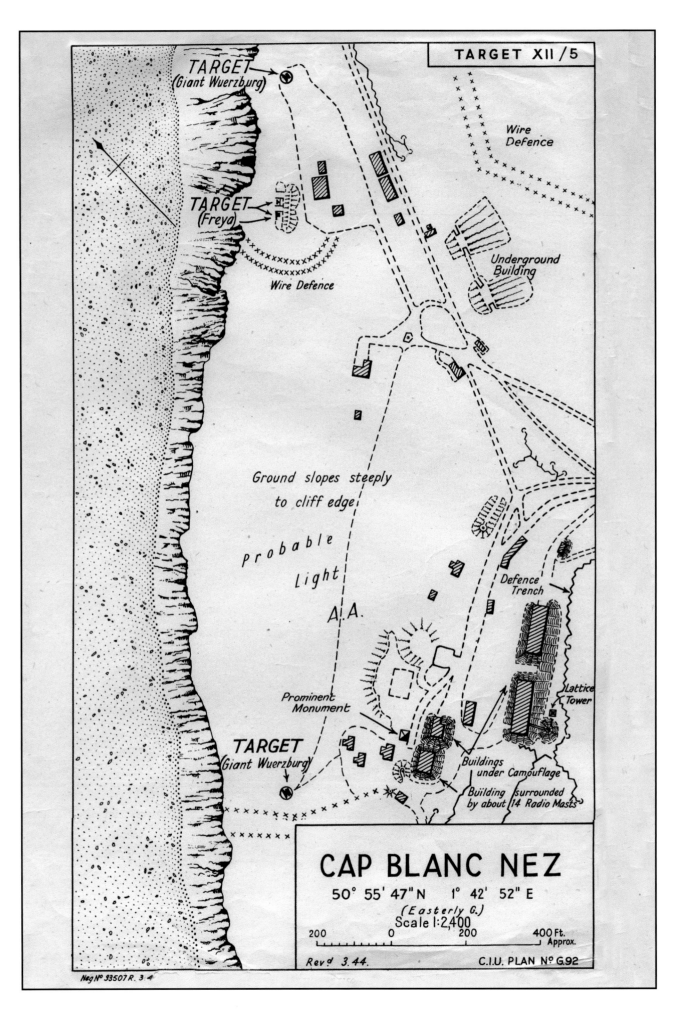

TARGET XII/5

TARGET
(Giant Wuerzburg)

Wire
Defence

TARGET
(Freya)

Underground
Building

Wire Defence

Ground slopes steeply
to cliff edge

Probable
Light
A.A.

Defence
Trench

Lattice
Tower

Prominent
Monument

TARGET
(Giant Wuerzburg)

Buildings
under Camouflage

Building surrounded
by about 14 Radio Masts

CAP BLANC NEZ
50° 55' 47"N   1° 42' 52" E
(Easterly G.)
Scale 1:2,400

200   0   200   400 Ft.
                            Approx.

Rev⁴ 3.44.

C.I.U. PLAN Nº G.92

Neg Nº 33507 R. 3.4

Observatory

Building surrounded
by masts

Monument

TARGET

CAP BLANC NEZ

Light A.A.

Though many of the concrete bases of the 'targets' are still existing today, many of them are now lost in scrublands or woods, so very difficult to trace. Others were simply removed by farmers when they proved a nuisance in their fields. Also, some were removed when the area was wholly reconstructed. Another difficulty is that there were so many German constructions in certain spots that it is very difficult to pin-point a Würzburg concrete base from the many Flak positions all around, and the craters left by the bombs when the RAF and US Air Force attacked the site. To help in the quest, we carefully checked aerials taken just post-war by the Institut Géographique National. Dating from 1946, 1947 or 1949 these photos clearly show all the German constructions still in existence. Matching these IGN aerials with the wartime aerials and the sketch plans by the Central Interpretation Unit enabled us to precisely pin-point each location.

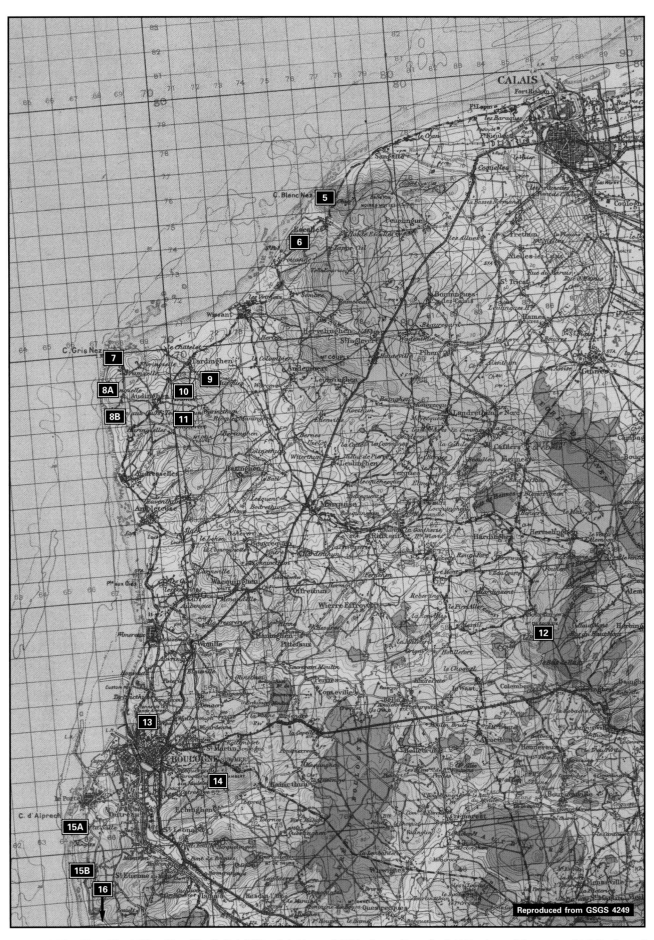

Targets: [5] Cap Blanc-Nez. [6] Cap Blanc-Nez/St Pol. [7] Cap Gris-Nez. [8] Cap Gris-Nez/Pointe du Riden. [9] Cap Gris-Nez/Bellevue. [10] Cap Gris-Nez/Wattermel St George. [11] Cap Gris-Nez/Onglevert. [12] Boulogne/Boursin. [13] Boulogne/Monument. [14] Boulogne/Mont Lambert. [15A] Boulogne/Cap d'Alprech. [15B] Boulogne/Cap d'Alprech. [16] Boulogne/Hardelot (off map).

A few hundred yards from the Dover Patrol Monument lay Target XII/6 — a small Würzburg on the cliff-top.

CAP BLANC-NEZ/ST POL

COASTAL SHIP-WATCHING STATION

Co-ordinates: 50° 54'49"N 1° 41' 41"E
Grid reference: 757742
Altitude: 215ft

Situated in open fields, about 200 yards from the cliff edge at a spot ¾ of a kilometre north-east of the seaside resort of St Pol, and approximately eight miles from Calais. It lies behind and to the south of a conspicuous wired-off site close to the cliff edge, presumably a defence site.

The target is a single, small Würzburg used as a Coastwatcher, standing in a shallow concrete emplacement.

From the target a slit trench leads some yards seaward. The Germans simply referred to it as 'Peilstand 3' (Radar site 3).

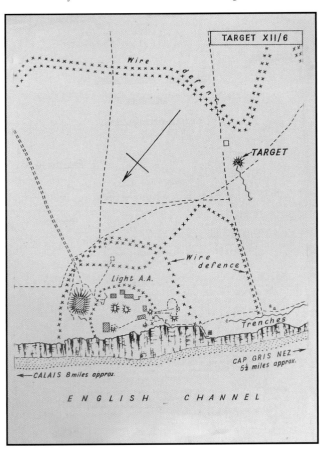

LIGHTHOUSE → SEMAPHORE STATION TARGET →

TARGET

CAP GRIS NEZ

View looking South.

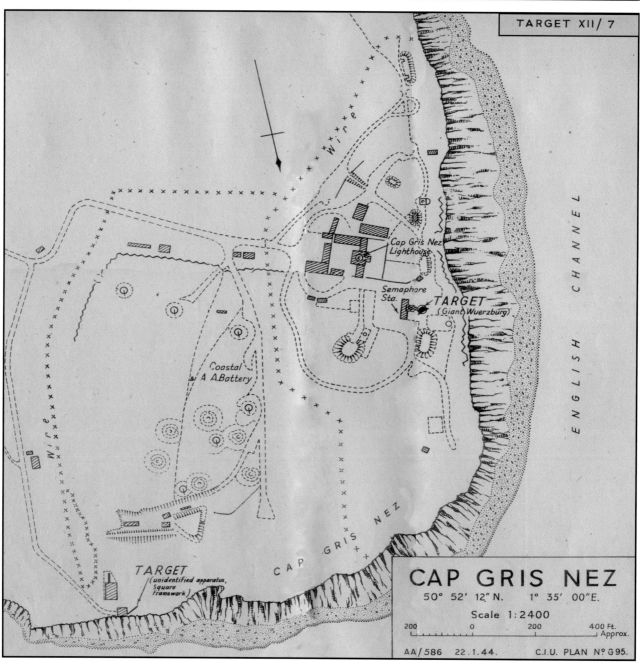

TARGET XII / 7

Wire

Cap Gris Nez
Lighthouse

Semaphore
Sta.

TARGET
(Giant Wuerzburg)

Coastal
A.A.Battery

Wire

ENGLISH CHANNEL

CAP GRIS NEZ

TARGET
(unidentified apparatus,
Square
framework)

CAP GRIS NEZ

50° 52' 12" N.   1° 35' 00" E.

Scale 1:2400

200   0   200   400 Ft.
                                    Approx.

AA/586   22.1.44.   C.I.U. PLAN Nº G95.

CAP GRIS-NEZ

COASTAL SHIP-WATCHING STATION

Co-ordinates: 50° 52'12"N 1° 35' 00" E
Grid reference: 675699
Altitude: 165ft

Target XII/7 is situated at the old semaphore station, 96 yards north-west of the lighthouse.

It consists of one Giant Würzburg and an unidentified apparatus. The Giant stands on the roof of a concrete casemate on the seaward side of, and adjoining, the old semaphore station.

The area is protected by a single belt of wire, surrounding the site as well as the AA position nearby.

North-east of the Giant on the extreme edge of the cliff's north face is an unidentified apparatus consisting of a narrow vertical framework measuring 44 feet across and about 40ft high.

Code-named 'Bumerang', the Würzburg Riese stood on the roof of the Battery Command Post for the 280mm (11-inch) 'Grosser Kurfürst' battery at Framezelle. This area was captured on September 29, 1944 by the Highland Light Infantry of Canada.

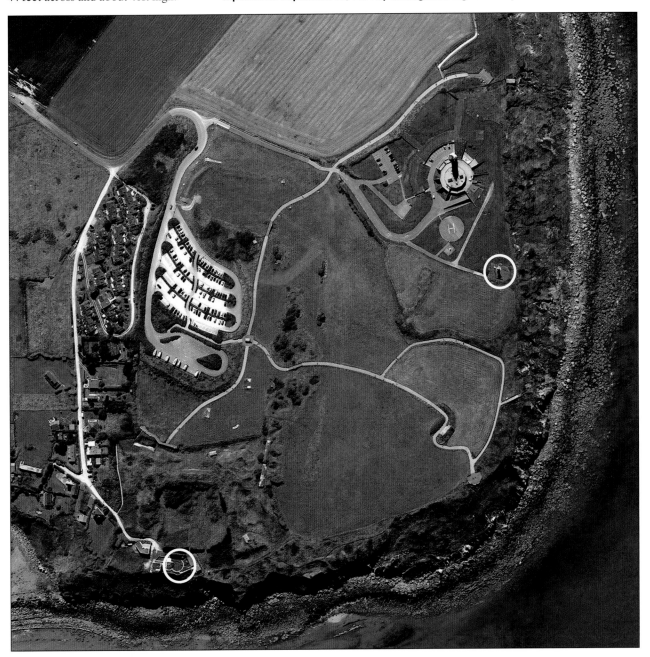

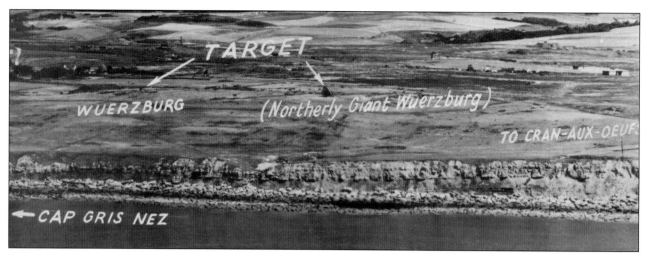

The CIU listed no less than five radar stations at or near Cap Gris-Nez. This is the northern site at Target XII/8.

CAP GRIS-NEZ/POINTE DU RIDEN

COASTAL SHIP-WATCHING STATION
Co-ordinates:
(SH): 50° 51'27"N 1° 35' 06" E
(G): 50° 50'52"N 1° 35' 08" E
Grid reference (SH): 675686, (G): 675675
Altitude (SH): 170ft, (G): 70ft

The site is dispersed over an elongated area near the edge of the cliffs between Cap Gris-Nez and Pointe Camberin, extending from a point 1,000 yards due south of the Cap Gris-Nez lighthouse to the southern side of the village of Cran-aux-Oeufs. The German code-name was 'Frundsberg'.

The target consists of a small Hoarding, two Giant Würzburgs and a small Würzburg, all of which are disposed in three separate sites. The most northerly of these sites is surrounded by a thick belt of wire and contains one of the Giants with, a few yards further north, the small Würzburg.

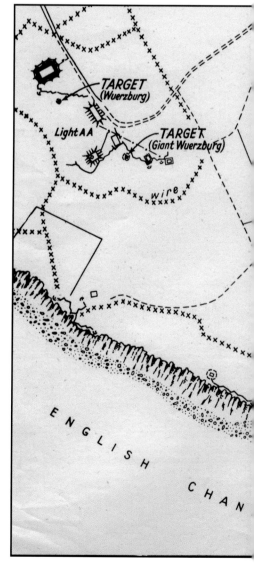

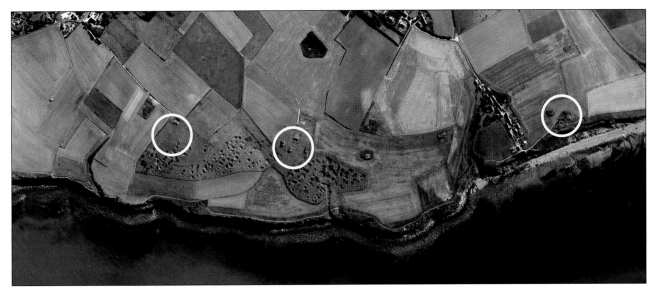

The three sites of Target XII/8 at Pointe du Riden pin-pointed today.

The second site (SH) is about 400 yards south of the first and 350 yards inland from the cliff edge, north-west of the village of Waringzelle. It is at present undefended by wire and contains the Hoarding, which is still in course of erection, on the seaward side of a group of huts and trenches. The third site (G) to the south of Cran-aux-Oeufs is about ¾ of a mile south of the second site and within a few yards of the cliff edge. It contains the second Giant Würzburg surrounded by wire and trenches. The whole area is well defended with light AA and machine guns.

Between the middle and southerly sites is a very conspicuous double belt of wire, surrounding a group of huts, which should not be mistaken for part of the target.

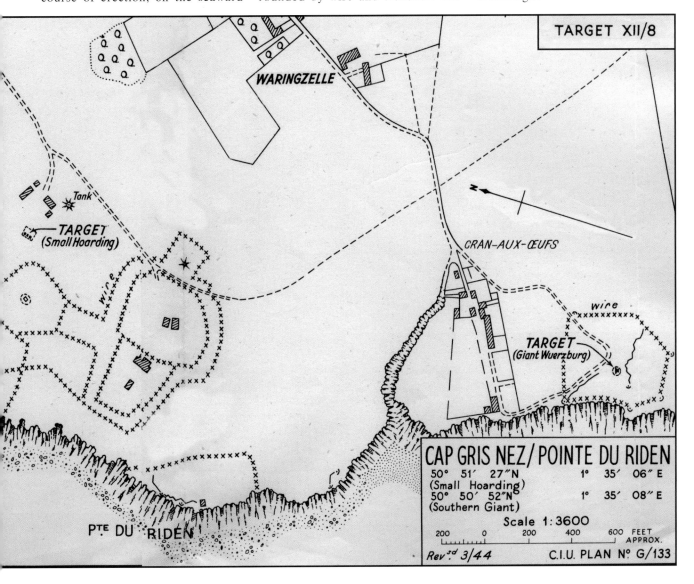

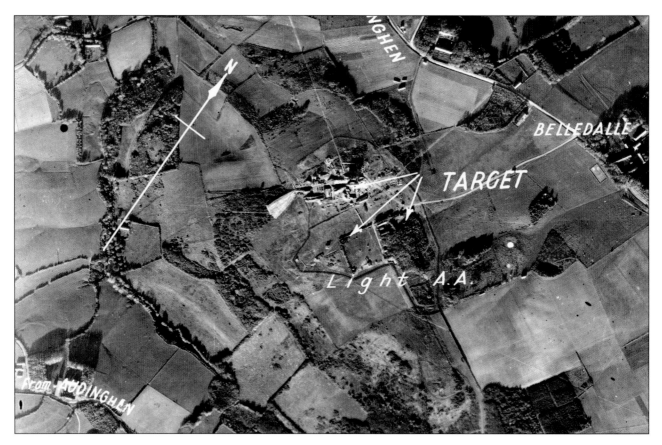

CAP GRIS-NEZ/BELLE-VUE

Target XII/9 was located at an inland site four kilometres from Cap Gris-Nez, off what is now the D249 north of Warincthun.

AIRCRAFT REPORTING STATION

Co-ordinates: 50° 51'31"N   1° 38' 25" E
Grid reference: 714684
Altitude: 260ft

The station is located midway between Audresselles on the south-west and Wissant to the north-east, and 2¾ miles east-south-east of Cap Gris-Nez. The nearest point on the coast is 1¾ miles to the north-north-west near La Belle Étoile.

It is situated in a small homestead on the north side of the summit of high ground, approximately 260ft above sea level, which rises from the south side of the road from Tardinghen to Audembert.

Target consists of a Hoarding and two Freyas which are disposed in the form of a triangle. The Hoarding surmounts a sunken building and is most conspicuous. Of the Freyas, one is housed in a square emplacement and surrounded by several operational huts, while the other is in a round emplacement centrally placed between three masts 50ft high.

A great deal of excavation has taken place, and some still continues, from which there is a good deal of spoil.

The site is extremely heavily defended with several rows of wire, slit trenches, light AA and machine guns.

Although this station on the Mont Plouvin height was an important link in the coastal chain, with both Freya and Hoarding installations, it has since been virtually erased from the map by the expansion of the wooded area.

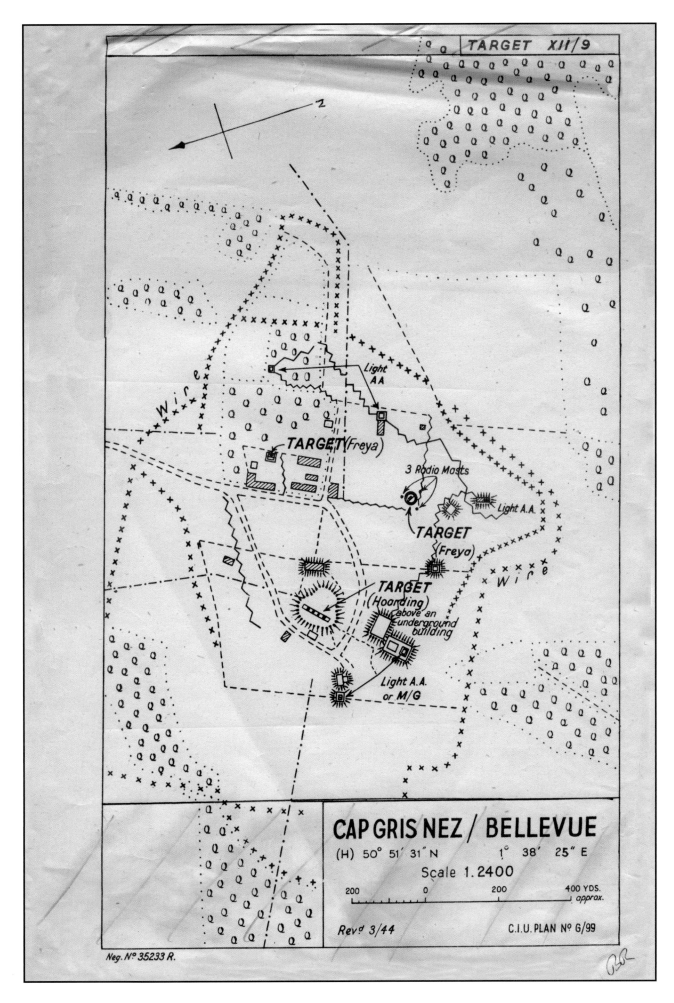

Light
AA

TARGET (Freya)

3 Radio Masts

Light A.A.

TARGET
(Freya)

TARGET
(Hoarding)
above an
underground
building

Wire

Wire

Light A.A.
or M/G

CAP GRIS NEZ / BELLEVUE

(H) 50° 51′ 31″ N   1° 38′ 25″ E

Scale 1.2400

200	0	200	400 YDS.

approx.

Revᵈ 3/44   C.I.U. PLAN Nº G/99

Neg. Nº 35233 R.

71

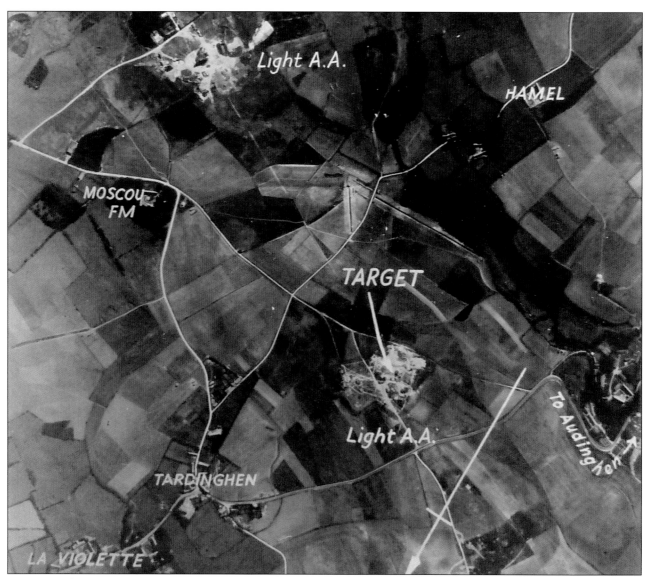

Light A.A.

HAMEL

MOSCOU FM

TARGET

Light A.A.

To Audinghen

TARDINGHEN

LA VIOLETTE

CAP GRIS-NEZ/WATTERMEL ST GEORGE

This photograph showing Target XII/10 at Wattermel St George is dated August 16, 1943.

AIRCRAFT REPORTING STATION

Co-ordinates: 50° 51'42"N 1° 37' 43"E
Grid reference: 706688
Altitude: 150ft

This position is midway between the villages of Tardinghen and Wattermel St George, south-east of Cap Gris-Nez, on a knoll just south-east of the road connecting the two villages.

This site is a few fields north-west of the big radar installation at Bellevue.

The target consists of a Giant Würzburg, standing in a circular concrete base, with a small operational hut beside it on the northern side.

It is heavily defended with trenches and wire, and is a site rendered conspicuous by constructional work still in progress.

Several other larger huts, machine gun posts, etc, surround the target.

The present-day aerial photograph is oriented the same as the wartime reconnaisance photo, the site, which straddled the road, being circled.

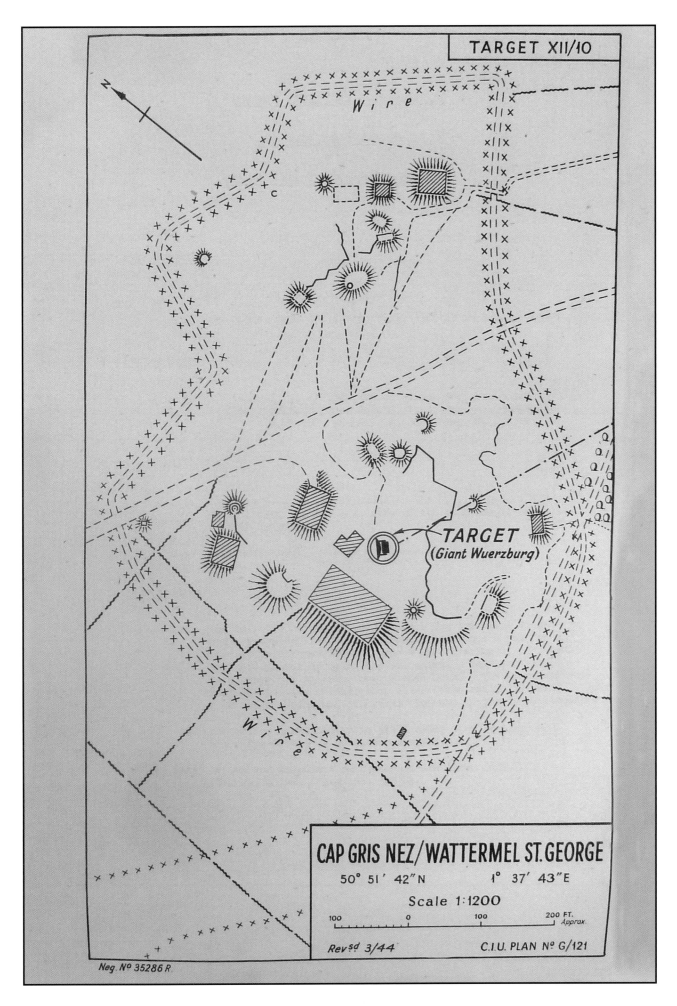

TARGET XII/10

Wire

C

TARGET
(Giant Wuerzburg)

Wire

CAP GRIS NEZ/WATTERMEL ST.GEORGE

50° 51′ 42″N   1° 37′ 43″E

Scale 1:1200

100   0   100   200 FT.
Approx.

Rev.sd 3/44   C.I.U. PLAN Nº G/121

Neg. Nº 35286 R.

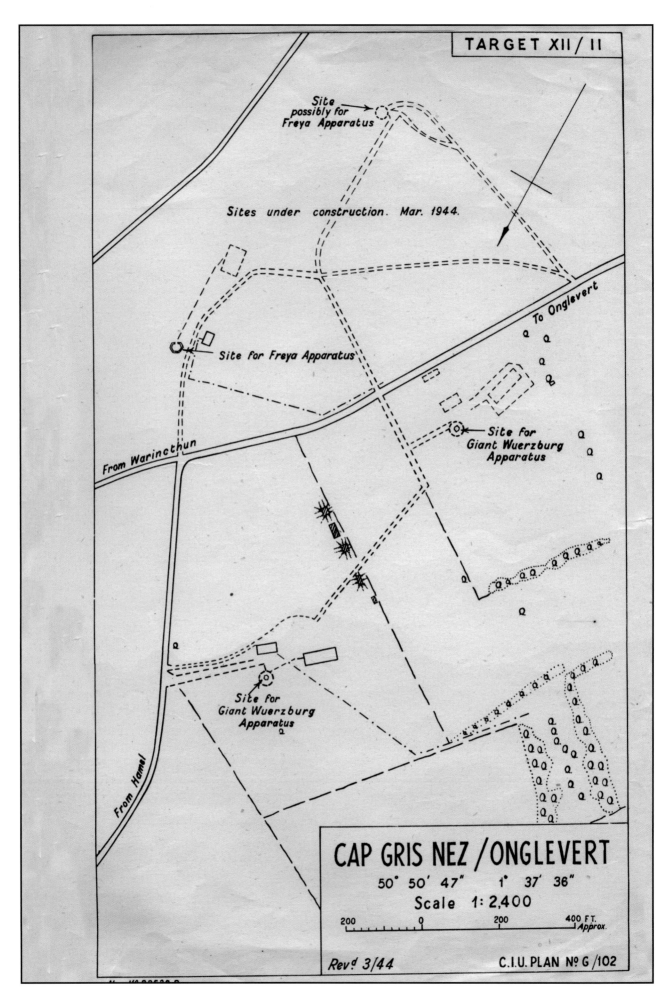

TARGET XII/II

Site possibly for Freya Apparatus

Sites under construction. Mar. 1944.

To Onglevert

Site for Freya Apparatus

From Warincthun

Site for Giant Wuerzburg Apparatus

Site for Giant Wuerzburg Apparatus

From Hamel

CAP GRIS NEZ/ONGLEVERT

50° 50′ 47″   1° 37′ 36″

Scale 1:2,400

200   0   200   400 FT. Approx.

Rev.d 3/44   C.I.U. PLAN N⁰ G/102

74

CAP GRIS-NEZ/ONGLEVERT

Target XII/11 at Onglevert was still undergoing construction on November 3, 1943. The arrow of North at bottom left is actually pointing due south.

GROUND CONTROL INTERCEPTION STATION

Co-ordinates: 50° 50'47"N 1° 37' 36"E
Grid reference: 703671
Altitude: 300ft

This station under construction lies 2½ miles south-east of Cap Gris-Nez on the north-west slopes of the Mont de la Louve, on the north-west side of the main road from Onglevert to Warinc-thun.

The target consists of emplacements for two Giant Würzburgs and a Freya apparatus. The former comprises a pair of concrete platforms 285 yards apart, the more southerly being the pin-point. Near each site is a generator and some operational huts.

The Freya emplacement is situated on the other side of the road, 270 yards from the pinpoint and 310 yards from the northerly emplacement.

The entire installation is still under construction, and there are little or no defences whatever.

The concrete bases of the two Würzburg radars still stand today in open fields and clearly show up on the Google Earth comparison. The German code-name for this station was 'Eber'.

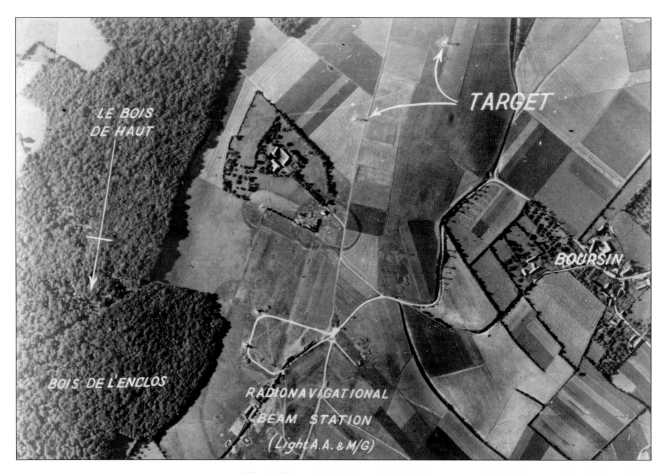

BOULOGNE/BOURSIN

DAY FIGHTER CONTROL STATION

Latitude: 50° 46'15"N 1° 50' 32" E
Grid reference: 848576
Altitude: 560ft
German ID: 427

The station on Mont Boursin is ¾ mile north-east of the village of Boursin and 10¾ miles east-north-east of Boulogne. It stands at the north of the summit of high ground, with well-wooded slopes called the Bois de l'Enclos to the east of it.

Target XII/12 consists of two tall lattice pylons about 60 feet high in open fields just south of the radio-navigational beam station (for day fighter direction) and separated from it by a farmstead. The more north-erly pylon is on the edge of a minor road running southward, the south-erly pylon is slightly to the west of this road.

The base of the most southerly pylon is still visible today, but no trace of the other one.

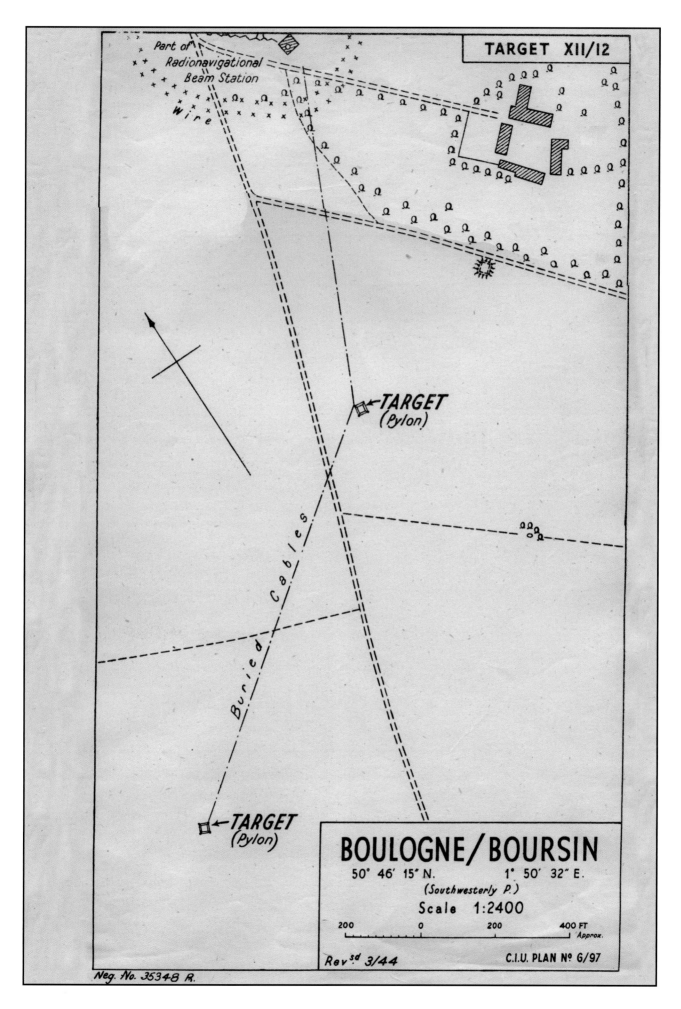

TARGET XII/12

Part of
Radionavigational
Beam Station

Wire

TARGET
(Pylon)

Buried Cables

TARGET
(Pylon)

BOULOGNE/BOURSIN

50° 46' 15" N.   1° 50' 32" E.
(Southwesterly P.)
Scale   1:2400

200   0   200   400 FT
Approx.

Rev^sd 3/44   C.I.U. PLAN Nº G/97

Neg. No. 35348 R.

77

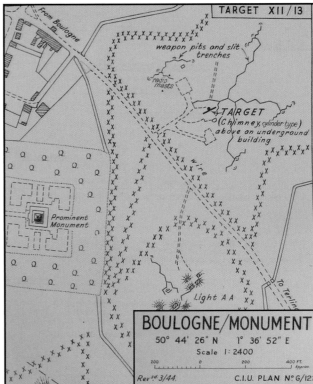

BOULOGNE/MONUMENT

AIRCRAFT REPORTING STATION

Latitude: 50° 44'26"N 1° 36' 52" E
Grid reference: 685555
Altitude: 300ft

Situated immediately west of the Monument de la Grande Armée, about 1½ miles north-north-east of Boulogne, and just west of the minor road running between Marlborough and Terlincthun, on the seaward side of the monument, and standing back some distance from the road.

The target consists of Chimney radar apparatus of Cylinder type (Wassermann) and a very small two-masted communication station situated directly east of it.

The site is defended by slit trenches and mines on the seaward side and is enclosed by wire defences.

In 1804, Napoléon gave orders for a triumphal monument to be erected in Boulogne to commemorate the successful invasion of England . . . something that he never aspired to! Instead, it was dedicated to 'the Grande Armée' although the statue of the Emperor himself — positioned facing away from England — was not installed on top of the column until 1841, 20 years after his death.

A hundred years later another dictator with designs of invading England was now on the scene, and his air force chose a site just to the rear of the column for a Chimney radar, the Germans giving it the code-name of 'Krokus'.

BOULOGNE/MONT LAMBERT

COASTAL SHIP-WATCHING STATION

Coordinates: 50° 43'09"N 1° 39' 07" E
Grid reference: 709528
Altitude: 600ft

Located on the north-east side of the old fort on the summit of Mont Lambert about two miles east of Boulogne. The outlines of this fort have now disappeared under new construction.

Target consists of a small hut carrying a frame aerial array of Coastwatcher type, enclosed entirely within a tall octagonal cylinder about 30 feet in diameter, partly mounded up with earth on the outside.

Immediately alongside, and behind, extensive military construction makes the site very conspicuous.

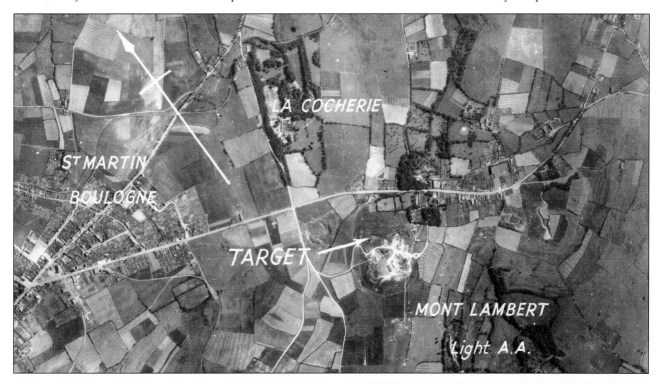

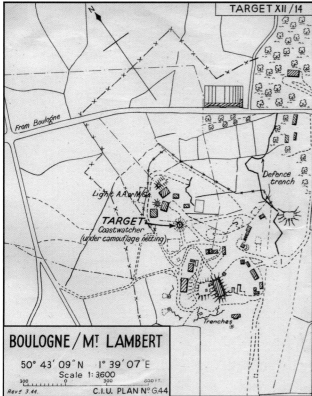

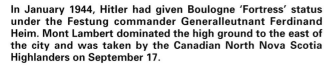

In January 1944, Hitler had given Boulogne 'Fortress' status under the Festung commander Generalleutnant Ferdinand Heim. Mont Lambert dominated the high ground to the east of the city and was taken by the Canadian North Nova Scotia Highlanders on September 17.

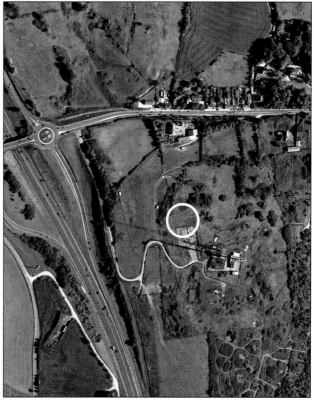

Today, with a tenuous link with the past, the summit of 620-foot-high Mont Lambert is crowned with broadcast aerials for radio, television and mobile telephones. The A16 motorway also carves a route close to the site of the old German radar station.

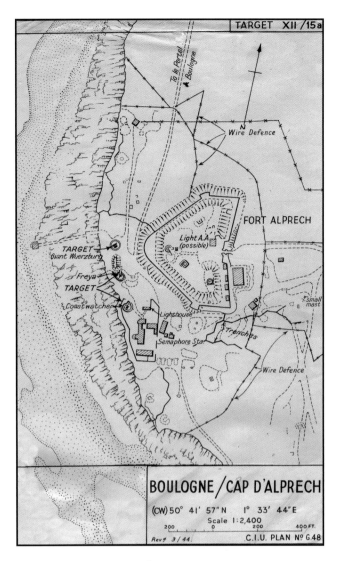

TARGET XII /15a

FORT ALPRECH

Light A.A.
(possible)

TARGET
Giant Wuerzburg

Freya

TARGET

Coastwatcher

Lighthouse

Semaphore Sta.

Trenches

Wire Defence

Wire Defence

small
mast

BOULOGNE/CAP D'ALPRECH

(CW) 50° 41' 57" N   1° 33' 44" E

Scale 1:2,400

200   0   200   400 FT.

Revg 3/44.   C.I.U. PLAN Nº G.48

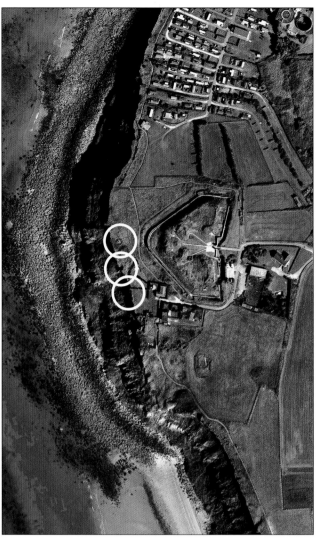

BOULOGNE/CAP D'ALPRECH

The CIU at Medmenham listed two radar stations south of Boulogne, identifying them as 'A' and 'B'. For the first one the Germans had used the 19th-century fort at Cap d'Alprech.

COASTAL SHIP-WATCHING STATION

Coordinates: 50° 41'57"N 1° 33' 44" E
Grid reference: 645511
Altitude: 140ft

Target 15A is situated a few yards from the cliff edge at Cap d'Alprech and immediately in front of Fort Alprech, 2½ miles south-west of the centre of Boulogne.

It consists of three apparatuses, viz: a Giant Würzburg situated directly in front of (west of) Fort Alprech, a Freya set a few yards further south, and a Coastwatcher directly in front of the lighthouse adjacent to the semaphore station immediately south of Fort Alprech.

The joint site of the targets, the fort and the semaphore station is defended by double belts of wire, and by trenches on the southerly, inland side. There is a possible light AA position on top of the fort.

The Freya and the Coastwatcher stand in low circular concrete emplacements. The Coastwatcher has a low wall between it and the cliff edge and might at first appear to be part of the semaphore station.

The view looking south at Target XII/15A on July 27, 1943. The German code-name for the station was 'Pantoffelblume'.

FORET DE BOULOGNE

TARGETS

Hangar

80

So few photographs are available from the German side that finding images suitable for genuine comparisons has not been easy. No caption is given for this photo other than 'France 1944' but the Giant Würzburg appears to be situated overlooking the sea, very much like the surviving base at Target XII/15A sited on the cliff-top at Cap d'Alprech.

BOULOGNE/ CAP D'ALPRECH

COASTAL SHIP-WATCHING STATION

Coordinates: 50° 41'15"N 1° 34' 08" E
Grid reference: 649498
Altitude: 200ft

The site of Target 15B is located 2¾ miles south-south-west of Boulogne and a mile south of Cap d'Alprech, situated in fields 400 yards from the cliff edge.

The target is a Small Hoarding standing on three concrete pedestals. The site is rendered conspicuous by recent excavations. Only a small hut stands in the immediate vicinity.

Between the Hoarding and the sea is a Heavy AA site on the seaward side of which are slit trenches behind which is a double belt of wire.

Target XII/15B lies a few hundred yards away. It comprised what the RAF called a 'Small Hoarding' and the photography of March 1943 showed extensive earthworks. Technically, the FuMG 41/42 Mammut was the world's first phased array as it was made up of six to eight Freya antennas linked together giving it a range of up to 300 kilometres and to an altitude of 8,000 metres. Although the array was fixed, it could be 'steered' electronically. A heavy anti-aircraft battery was sited near the edge of the cliff, and traces of both it and the Hoarding site are still apparent.

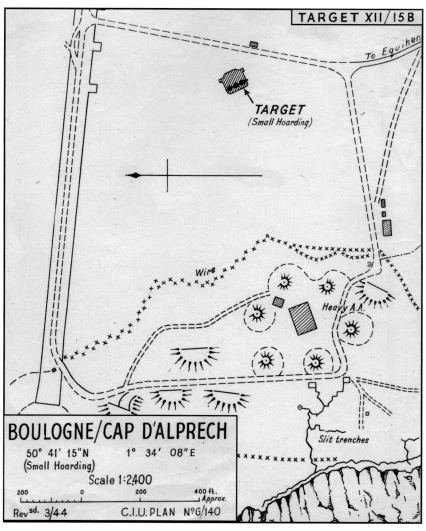

TARGET XII/15B

TARGET
(Small Hoarding)

To Equihen

Wire

Heavy A.A.

Slit trenches

BOULOGNE/CAP D'ALPRECH

50° 41' 15"N   1° 34' 08"E
(Small Hoarding)
Scale 1:2400

200   0   200   400 ft.
                                      Approx.

Rev.sd. 3/44   C.I.U. PLAN No.G/140

TARGET

Heavy A.A.

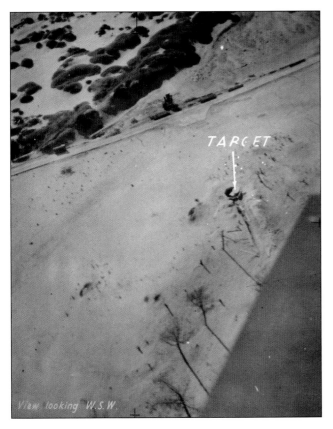

View looking W.S.W.

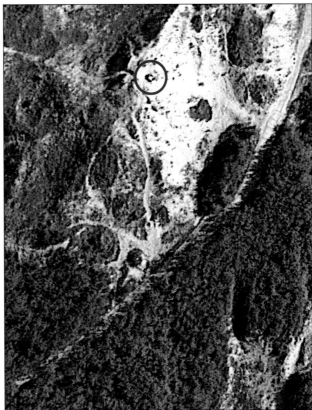

Target XII/16 was very difficult to locate, either on the ground or from the air as it merged into the dunes just north of Hardelot but the concrete base is still there.

BOULOGNE/HARDELOT

COASTAL SHIP-WATCHING STATION

Coordinates: 50° 39'04"N 1° 34' 51" E
Grid reference: 654457
Altitude: 80ft

This site was situated in the dunes a little way in from the foreshore, one mile due north of Hardelot, on the north side of a track leading from the coastline toward the wooded scrub further east.

The target consists of a small Würzburg used as a Coastwatcher standing in an octagonal concrete emplacement, the sides of which partially hide the apparatus. A single belt of wire surrounds the target.

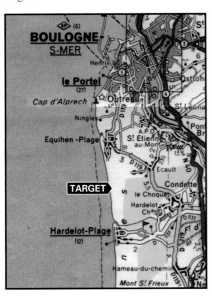

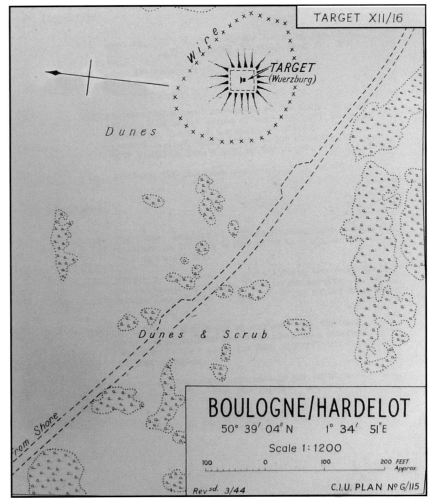

TARGET XII/16

TARGET (Wuerzburg)

Dunes

Dunes & Scrub

from Shore

BOULOGNE/HARDELOT
50° 39' 04" N   1° 34' 51"E
Scale 1:1200
100   0   100   200 FEET
Approx.

Rev'sd. 3/44   C.I.U. PLAN N° G/II5

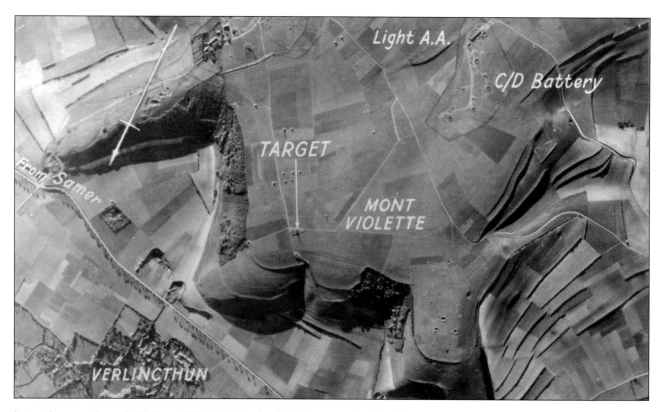

Instructions were issued with Target XII/17 that the site should not be confused with the much more conspicuous Knickebein radio-navigational beam station, also situated on Mont Violette which was visible some distance away to the south.

MONT VIOLETTE

AIRCRAFT REPORTING STATION

Coordinates: 50° 37'22"N 1° 40' 34" E
Grid reference: 719420
Altitude: 585ft

Inland from the Hardelot site, and situated at a minor crossroads on the north-north-east edge of the plateau on the summit of Mont Violette, due east of Neufchâtel, the target lies south of the Fôret d'Hardelot. The nearest village, Verlincthun, on low ground north of Mont Violette, lies north-north-east of the target.

This consists of a Freya standing in an octagonal concrete emplacement beside which is a single blast-wall-protected hut.

On the north side there are three defence trenches, two on the hillcrest and one close to the target. A single line of wire defends the target on the south side.

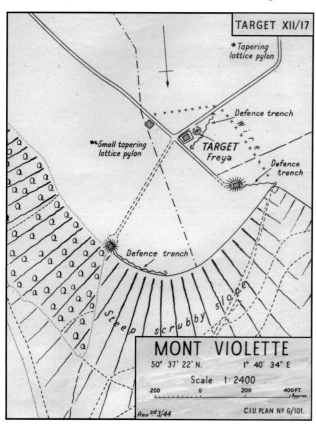

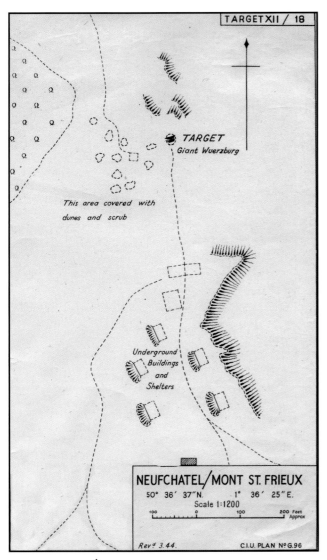

A very strong 'Stützpunktgruppe', with several bunkers and gun emplacements, was also located on the summit of Mont St Frieux, some 200 metres north-east of Target XII/18.

NEUFCHÂTEL/MONT ST FRIEUX

COASTAL SHIP-WATCHING STATION

Coordinates: 50° 36'37"N 1° 36' 25" E
Grid reference: 669410
Altitude: 350ft

The radar installation is situated on a commanding site in the dunes 1½ miles west-south-west of Neufchâtel, on the coastal side, and just below the summit of the hill named Mont St Frieux which rises to about 400 feet, about 1½ miles from the coastline. The targets consists of a single Giant Würzburg, unemplaced and set on a circular concrete base.

We have included this early post-war photograph to aid the precise location where the Giant Würzburg stood.

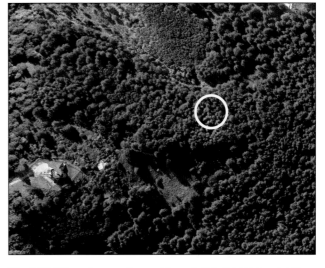

Mont St Frieux is now topped by a tall telecommunications tower.

85

LE TOUQUET/PLAGE STE CÉCILE

An elaborate radar site was built just north of the estuary of the Canche at Le Touquet. The Central Interpretation Unit at Medmenham split the site between the Freyas and the Würzburgs.

AIRCRAFT REPORTING STATION

Coordinates (F): 50° 34'26"N 1° 34' 42" E
Grid reference (F): 644372
Altitude (F): 13ft
Coordinates (G): 50° 34'32"N 1° 35' 11" E
Grid reference (G): 650373
Altitude (G): 23ft

Situated at the Plage Ste Cécile, a little seaside resort 3¾ miles north by west of Le Touquet church.

The position (F) is south of the Plage Ste Cécile: the position (G) is dispersed to the north of the road and the few houses still standing.

Target (F) consists of two Freyas. Of these, the more southerly is the pin-point, and is in a circular built-up emplacement, camouflaged as a hillock in the dunes. The second Freya is 200 yards north and nearer the village. It is on a high part of the dunes and is standing in a circular concrete emplacement. Net camouflage has been put up to conceal this site. A large building stands between the two emplacements.

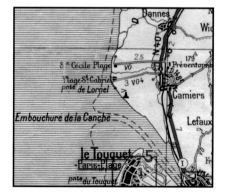

The maps, dated 50 years apart, show the transformation from sandy dunes to holiday resort.

Target (G) consists of two Giant Würzburgs and a small Würzburg. These are all at some distance from the shore and roughly north-east of the Freya apparatus. The pin-point (G) refers to the southerly Giant which is 700 yards from the shore and set on a hillock, possibly artificial, higher than the nearby houses. The second Giant is 260 yards north of the pin-point, away from houses and stands on a raised position in the dunes. Beneath both these Giants are concrete shelters, and there are two operational huts close to the more northerly apparatus. The small Würzburg is situated 260 yards west-north-west of the second Giant, at the northern end of the north to south road through Plage Ste Cécile.

LE ROUART

CAMIERS

DANNES

TO →
ETAPLES

TARGETS

PLAGE ST. GABRIE

PLAGE
ST. CECILY

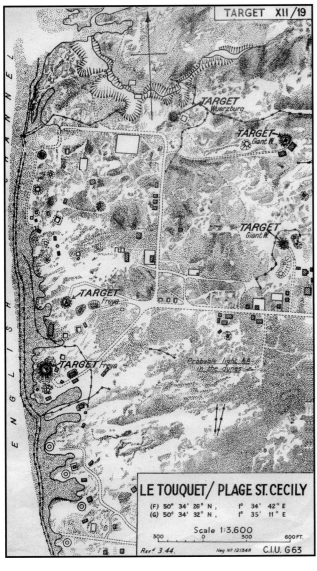

TARGET XII/19

CHANNEL

ENGLISH

TARGET
Wuerzburg

TARGET
Giant W.

TARGET
Giant W.

TARGET
Freya

TARGET Freya

Probable light AA
in the dunes

TARGET Freya

LE TOUQUET/ PLAGE ST.CECILY

(F) 50° 34' 26" N , 1° 34' 42" E
(G) 50° 34' 32" N , 1° 35' 11" E

Scale 1:3.600

300   0   300   600 FT.

Rev.d 3.44.   Neg N° 12134R   C.I.U. G 63

With post-war development at Ste Cécile Plage having totally
obliterated the area, the components of Target XII/19 have
completely disappeared beneath the housing. To the Germans
this station was code-named 'Bulldogge'.

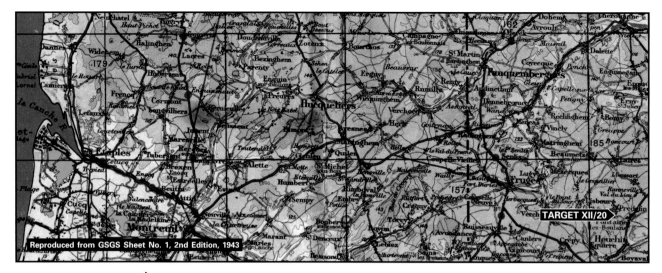

Reproduced from GSGS Sheet No. 1, 2nd Edition, 1943

TARGET XII/20

FRUGES/PRÉDEFIN

Target XII/20 lay 35 miles inland from the coast at Étaples. It consisted of two Giant Würzburgs, a Freya and a Hoarding. Hutments, one being 'Z'-shaped (which still survives), lay within the site which was defended with a perimeter of barbed wire.

AIRCRAFT REPORTING STATION

Coordinates (G): 50° 29'43"N 2° 15' 32" E
Grid reference (G): 119247
Altitude (G): 520ft
Coordinates (H): 50° 29'39"N 2° 15' 02" E
Grid reference (H): 113247
Altitude (H): 520ft

The site is on the summit of high ground about ¾ mile to the south of the village of Prédefin, 5½ miles east-south-east of Fruges. The target is on a southerly extension of this high ground, and on all sides except the north the land falls gently. Several minor roads cross the area.

The target consists of two Giant Würzburgs, a Freya and a Hoarding. The Giant pin-point (G), is situated just north of a small wood 1½ miles north of Bergueneuse, and is on the east side of the minor road connecting this village with Prédefin. The second Giant is 406 yards east-north-east from the first.

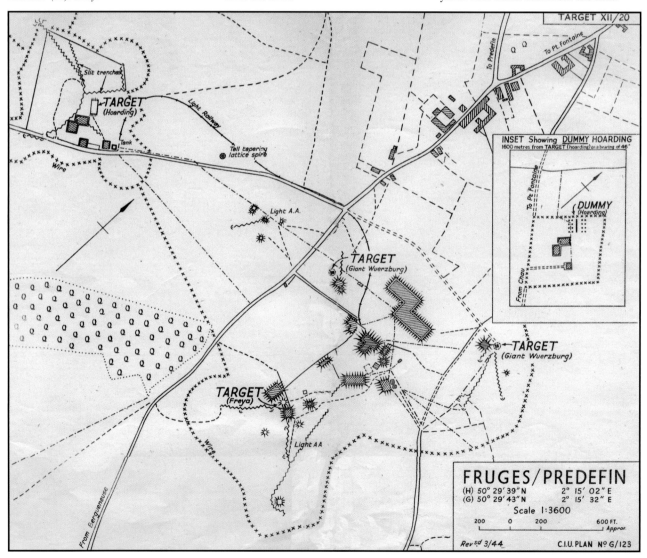

88

The Central Interpretation Unit identified what was believed to be a dummy site a mile away to the east. This was indicated on the target photography, although for some reason the annotations on the print were made upside down. We have printed the photo with north at the top to correspond with the plan and the Google Earth comparison *(below)*. On this we have circled the individual targets, the foundations of which still show up.

The Freya is in a circular raised emplacement 314 yards south-south-east of the first Giant. On the other (west) side of the road, and standing in a separately defended site, is the Hoarding, pinpoint (H). A tall temporary lattice tower, about 120 feet high, stands a short distance to the north-east of the Hoarding.

The sites are heavily defended with wire and light AA and the two Giants are each surrounded by a circular trench. There are sunken buildings close to each apparatus and slit trenches, running southwards, protecting the position of the Freya.

Situated one mile north-east of the target and east of Prédefin is a dummy Hoarding rendered conspicuous by eight small square blocks of concrete on either side.

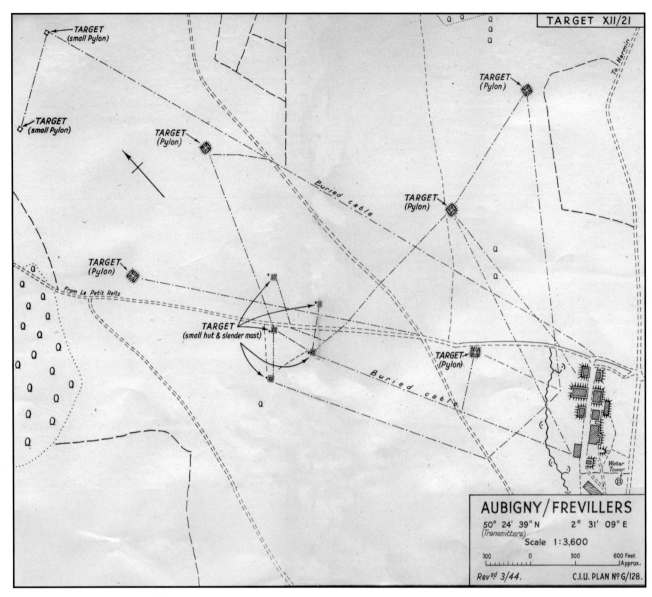

AUBIGNY/FREVILLERS
50° 24' 39"N   2° 31' 09" E
(Transmitters)
Scale 1:3,600

300   0   300   600 Feet
|_____|_____|_____|_____| Approx.

Rev^sd 3/44.   C.I.U. PLAN N° G/128.

AUBIGNY/FRÉVILLERS

Even further from the coast lay a day fighter control station comprising a number of pylons — very difficult to identify and destroy. Located not far from Arras, the station became CIU Target XII/21.

DAY FIGHTER CONTROL STATION

Coordinates: 50° 24'39"N 2° 31' 09" E
Grid reference: 296141
Altitude: 625ft

Situated on high ground, about ¾ of a mile north of the village of Frévillers and about 5¼ miles north-west of the town of Aubigny. The target is dispersed around a conspicuous acute-angled crossroads, and stretches from the outskirts of Frévillers to a long narrow strip of woodland just east of the target.

The target is a station consisting of seven tall lattice pylons, five of them about 60 feet high and two about 50 feet high. In addition, there are five small transmitter huts, each with a mast about 80 feet high. The displacement of the pylons is irregular and covers an area approximately 620 yards north to south and 510 yards east to west. The five transmitter huts are grouped regularly about 90 yards apart near the centre of the area.

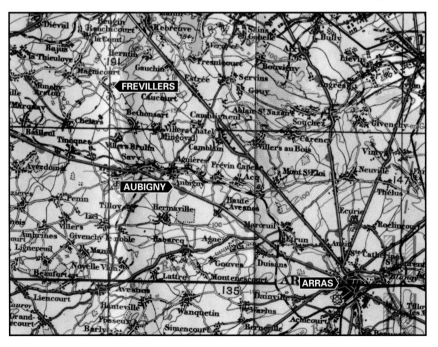

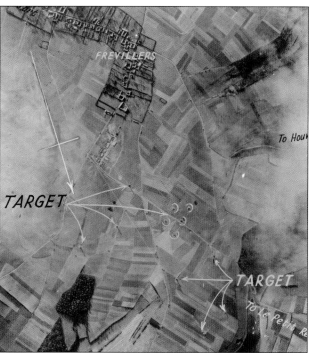

The headquarters buildings, situated between the village and the pylons, consisted of a double row of sunken bunkers.

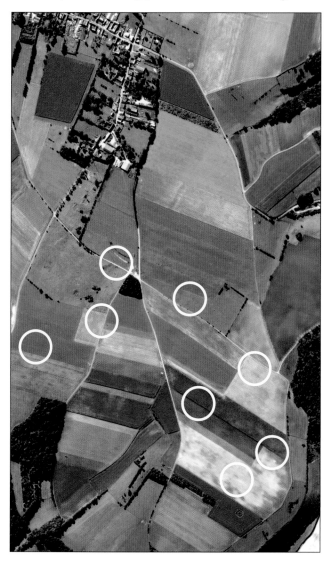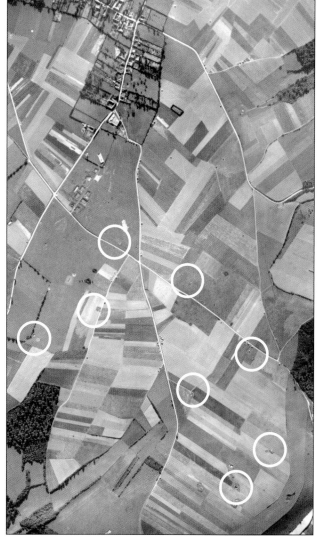

None of the targets can be seen on the present-day Google Earth *(left)* so we went back to 1947 to find photography showing the same area *(right)* before the local farmers began the restoration of the fields.

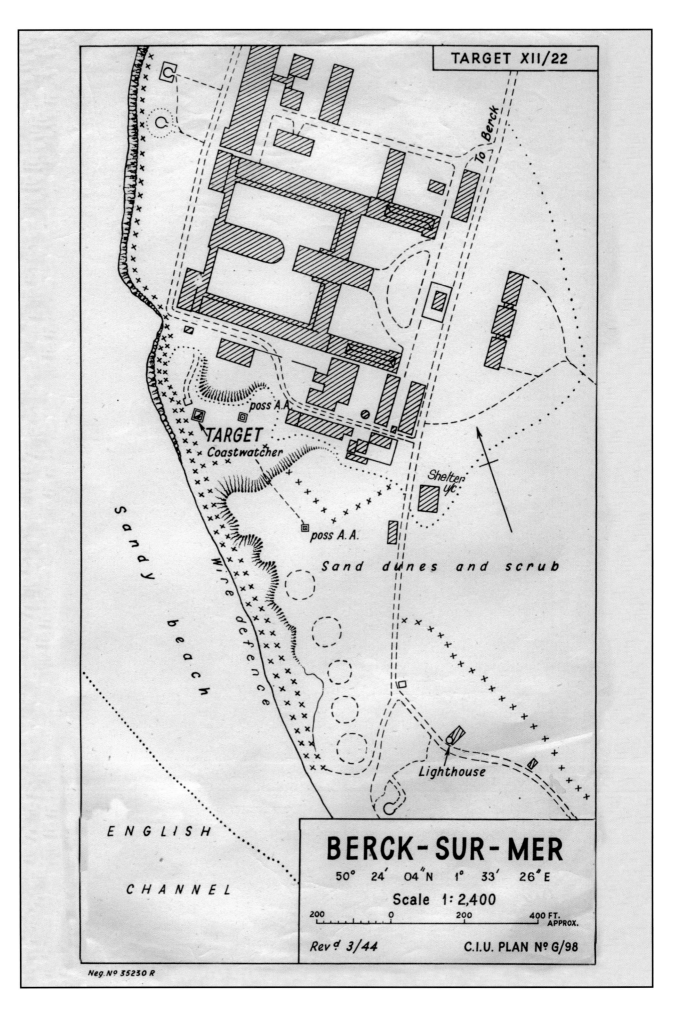

TARGET XII/22

To Berck

poss A.A.

TARGET
Coastwatcher

poss A.A.

Shelter
y/c

Sand dunes and scrub

Sandy beach

Wire defence

Lighthouse

ENGLISH

CHANNEL

BERCK-SUR-MER

50° 24′ 04″N   1° 33′ 26″E

Scale 1:2,400

200   0   200   400 FT.
APPROX.

Revᵈ 3/44   C.I.U. PLAN Nº G/98

Neg.Nº 35230 R

92

Air-launched rocket projectiles had been developed as weapons against ships and armoured fighting vehicles. There were two kinds: a 25lb solid armour-piercing head of 3.44ins in diameter, and a 6-inch 60lb semi-armour-piercing version. It was the latter with its high-explosive head which proved to be a most effective weapon against ground targets, concrete gun emplacements and buildings, etc., and it was used widely in the Normandy campaign. Here, an 'enemy radar installation in northern France' is under attack on D-Day itself.

BERCK-SUR-MER

COASTAL SHIP-WATCHING STATION

Coordinates: 50° 24'04"N 1° 33' 26" E
Grid reference: 614181
Altitude: 20ft

The station is located at the southern coastal extremity of Berck-sur-Mer, immediately south of a large group of buildings of conspicuous quadrangular layout, 360 yards north of the Berck lighthouse. On a high point in the dunes close to the seashore.

The target is a Coastwatcher standing in a square concrete emplacement in uneven surroundings of sand and scrub. Some distance behind it a large concrete shelter is under construction, and there is a possible AA site close by.

On the coastal side of the target are two rows of mines.

We now know that the attack was on Target XII/22 which stood just beside the General Hospital at Berck.

View looking E.S.E.

CAYEUX/NOUVEAU BRIGHTON

COASTAL SHIP-WATCHING STATION

Coordinate: 50° 11'47"N 1° 30' 42" E
Grid reference: 563958
Altitude: 2ft

This station is in a commanding position in the dunes on the south side of the mouth of the Somme at the seaside resort of Nouveau Brighton about ½ mile north of Cayeux. On the seaward side of the road running along the seafront it lies in front of the lighthouse and semaphore station.

Remains of the foundations of the Giant Würzburg on Nouveau Brighton beach can still to be seen at Cayeux.

The target consists of a Giant Würzburg used as a Coastwatcher, and rendered inconspicuous by its surroundings of dunes and scrub.

A fairly elaborate system of slit trenches crosses the site which is most probably enclosed by a belt of wire defences.

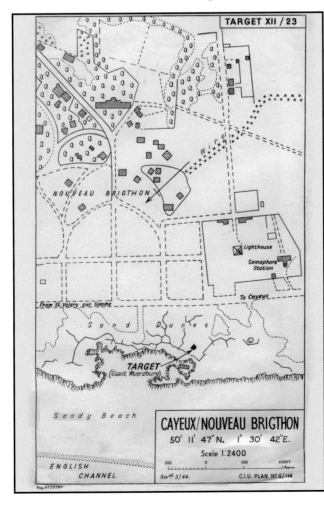

Fixed installations were always at risk of attack so, just as Germany adopted mobile launch facilities for the later V2 rocket, so Würzburgs were moved on rolling stock. This is a Würzburg Riese Eisenbahn-Ausführung (railway-mounted).

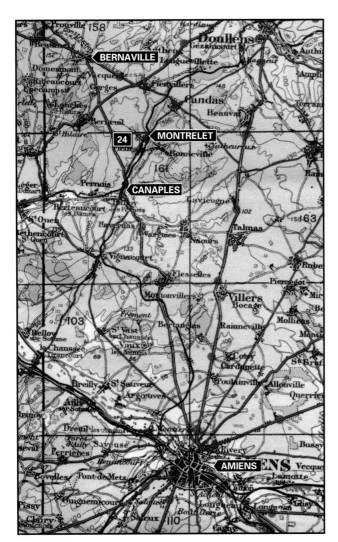

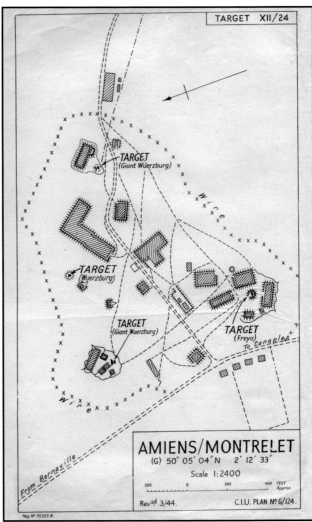

AMIENS/MONTRELET

GROUND CONTROL INTERCEPTION STATION

Coordinates: 50° 05'04"N 2° 12' 33" E
Grid reference: 051795
Altitude: 460ft

This complex is located 22 miles north-north-west of Amiens and 1½ miles west of the village of Montrelet, on the east side of, and adjoining, the minor road running from Bernaville southward toward Canaples and Amiens.

The target consists of two Giant Würzburgs, one Freya and one small Würzburg. The coordinate refers to the more southerly Giant, the other being 300 yards away on a bearing of 285 degrees true.

Adjacent to each apparatus is a long hut. Midway between the Giants is a large L-shaped hut on the west side of which is the small Würzburg. The Freya stands in an earth-mounded emplacement on the southern side of the installation, 300 yards from the pin-point on a bearing of 238 degrees true.

The whole area is protected by wire; the Freya and two Giants, together with their adjacent buildings, are surrounded by slit trenches, rifle pits and individual belts of wire.

Ground control interception stations usually lay well inland (see the maps on pages 19-20 and 48-49) and Montelet, over 40 miles from the coast, was no exception.

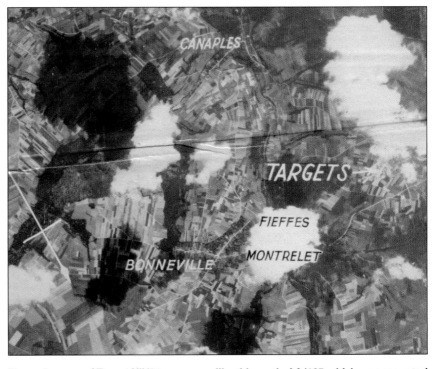

The early cover of Target XII/24 was poor, like this sortie AA/185 which was mounted on July 28, 1943.

The site was re-photographed on October 22 with somewhat better results but still with some cloud cover.

The map co-ordinates given by the CIU marked the southerly Giant but today it looks as if the installation never existed.

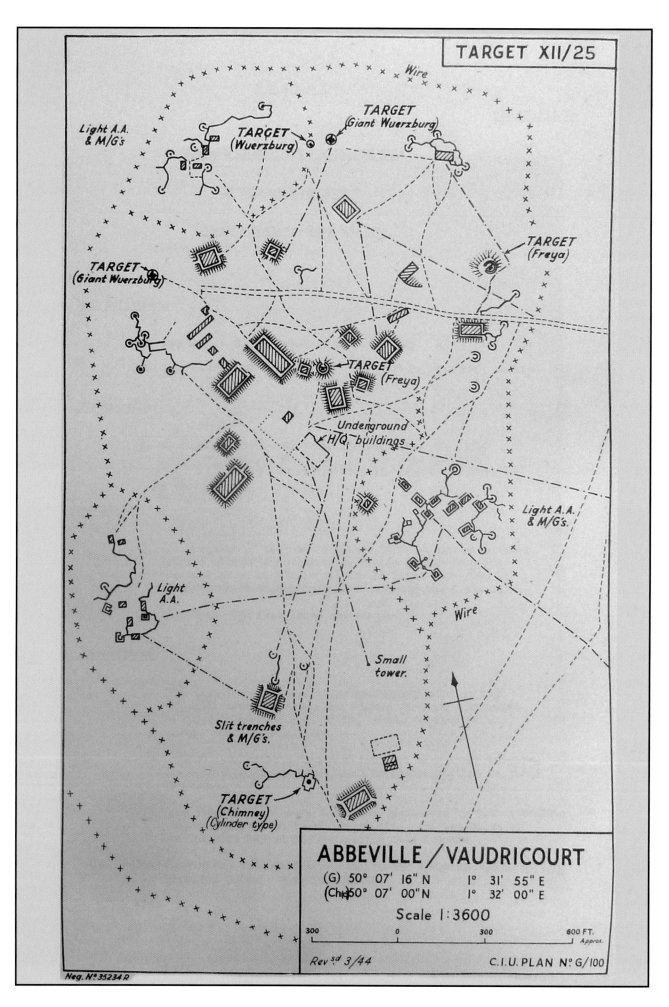

TARGET XII/25

Wire

Light A.A.
& M/G's

TARGET
(Wuerzburg)

TARGET
(Giant Wuerzburg)

TARGET
(Freya)

TARGET
(Giant Wuerzburg)

TARGET
(Freya)

Underground
H/Q buildings

Light A.A.
& M/G's.

Wire

Light
A.A.

Small
tower.

Slit trenches
& M/G's.

TARGET
(Chimney)
(Cylinder type)

ABBEVILLE / VAUDRICOURT

(G) 50° 07' 16" N   1° 31' 55" E
(Ch) 50° 07' 00" N   1° 32' 00" E

Scale 1:3600

300   0   300   600 FT.
Approx.

Rev ᵈ 3/44   C.I.U. PLAN Nº G/100

Neg. Nº 35234 R

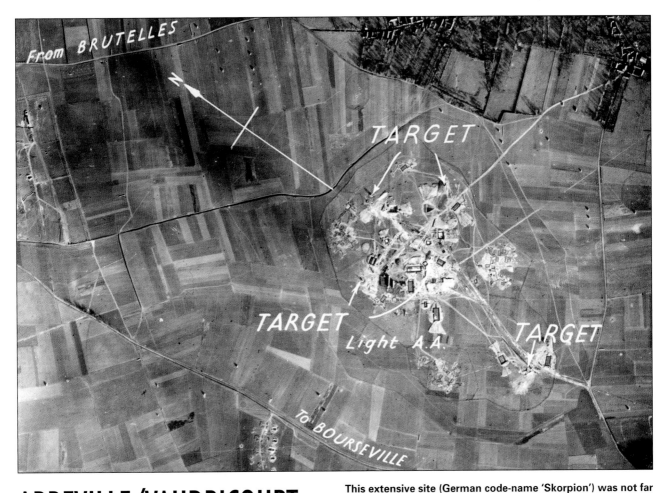

ABBEVILLE/VAUDRICOURT

This extensive site (German code-name 'Skorpion') was not far from the coast just south of the estuary of the River Somme; another station that has virtually disappeared from the map.

AIRCRAFT REPORTING STATION

Coordinates (CH): 50° 07'00"N 1° 32' 00" E
Grid reference (CH): 571868
Coordinates (G): 50° 07'16"N 1° 31' 55" E
Grid reference (G): 571873
Altitude: 165ft

This station is three miles inland and about five miles south of the mouth of the Somme, 14 miles west of Abbeville, and about four miles east-north-east of the seaside town of Ault, on high ground just west of the village of Vaudricourt.

Target consists of a pair of Giant Würzburgs, two Freyas, a small Würzburg and a Chimney of Cylinder type (Wassermann). The pin-points (G) and (CH) refer to the more southerly Giant and the Chimney respectively. The two Giants are on the north and north-west outskirts of the wired area occupied by the installation, and stand on circular concrete bases surrounded by a trench. They are 290 yards apart on a bearing of 60 degrees true. Close to the northerly Giant is the small Würzburg in a slightly built-up emplacement.

Of the Freyas, one of 'Pole' type is on the north-east side of the installation in an emplacement set on top of a raised earth mound; the other, of 'Limber' type is in the centre of the installation amongst a group of sunken huts. The latter stands in an octagonal emplacement on an earth mound.

The Chimney is at the extreme south end of the area between a sunken hut and a slit trench.

The whole site is heavily defended with light AA machine guns, trenches and wire defences.

Traces of the former station can just be discerned in the fields.

LE TREPORT/M.T HUON   TARGET XII/26

View looking South East

MONT HUON

Semaphore Station
building demolished

TARGETS

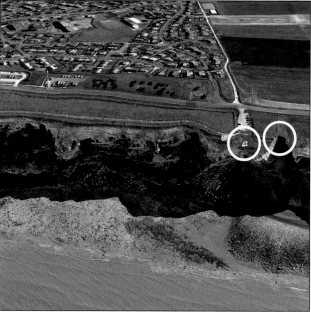

LE TRÉPORT/MONT HUON

Le Tréport was a small fishing village 20 miles north of Dieppe at the mouth of the Bresle river. The radar station lay on the 110-metre-high cliffs.

COASTAL SHIP-WATCHING STATION

Coordinates: 50° 03'29"N 1° 21' 38" E
Grid reference: 442813
Altitude: 330ft

Target stands at the site of the old semaphore station, now demolished, on the edge of the cliffs, less than ½ mile from the harbour at Le Tréport. It is the third site from Le Tréport where excavations have recently taken place.

It consists of a Coastwatcher placed on top of a concrete casemate, and a Giant Würzburg situated a short distance west-south-west of it, on the western side of a deeply trenched enclosure.

Several sunken buildings are situated near these targets, and the site of the demolished semaphore station is still visible.

The trenched enclosure is further protected by slit trenches, and weapon pits on the landward side, and two belts of barbed wire beyond the encircling main trench.

Reproduced from GSGS 4249 Sheet 9D

LE TRÉPORT

Mont-Huon

Mesnil-Sauren

Mancheville

Mesnil-Val Plocques

Le Quesnel

Etalondes

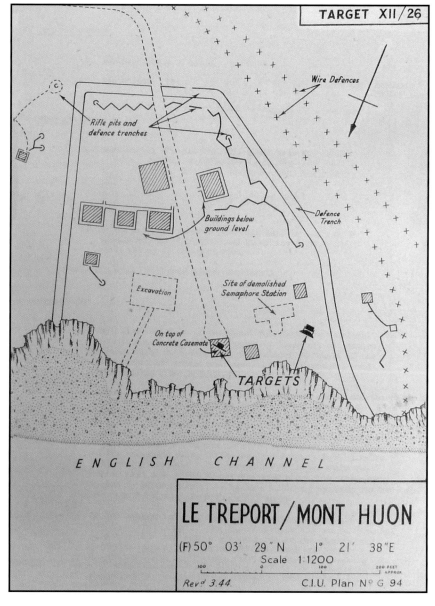

TARGET XII/26

Wire Defences

Rifle pits and defence trenches

Buildings below ground level

Defence Trench

Excavation

Site of demolished Semaphore Station

On top of Concrete Casemate

TARGETS

ENGLISH CHANNEL

LE TREPORT / MONT HUON

(F) 50° 03' 29" N   1° 21' 38" E
Scale 1:1200
100   100   200 FEET APPROX

Rev.d 3.44.   C.I.U. Plan N° G 94

DIEPPE/CAUDE-CÔTE

As part of the landings at Dieppe on August 19, 1942, the radar installation (Target XII/27) at Pourville behind Green Beach was singled out for capture.

AIRCRAFT REPORTING STATION

Latitude (F): 49° 55'20"N 1° 02' 52" E
Grid reference (F): 207682
Latitude (H): 49° 54'56"N 1° 03' 01" E
Grid reference (H): 208675
Altitude: 195ft

On the northern slope of the high land at Caude-Côte immediately west of Dieppe, and east of the fertile and woody valley of the Scie river.

The target consists of two Giant Würzburgs, a Hoarding, a small Würzburg, and two Freyas. These are all within a large wired enclosure occupying almost the whole of the Caude-Côte high ground and traversed by the coastal road between Dieppe and Pourville.

On the seaward side of this road are the two Freyas and the small Würzburg. The pin-point (F) refers to the more easterly Freya which stands on the extreme edge of hte cliff in a built-up square emplacement close to a site where excavations are taking place and spoil has been thrown out.

Directly behind this Freya and just at the edge of the excavated site, is the small Würzburg in a circular shallow emplacement. The second Freya is 340 yards west nearer (and some yards east of) the spot where the coast road begins to curve sharply; it is in a built-up concrete emplacement about 100 feet from the cliff edge.

Code-named 'Dickhäuter', it was manned by the 23. Kompanie of Luftgau-Nachrichten-Regiment Belgien-Nordfrankreich, which later became the 15. Flugmelde-Leit-Kompanie of Luftnachrichten-Regiment 52.

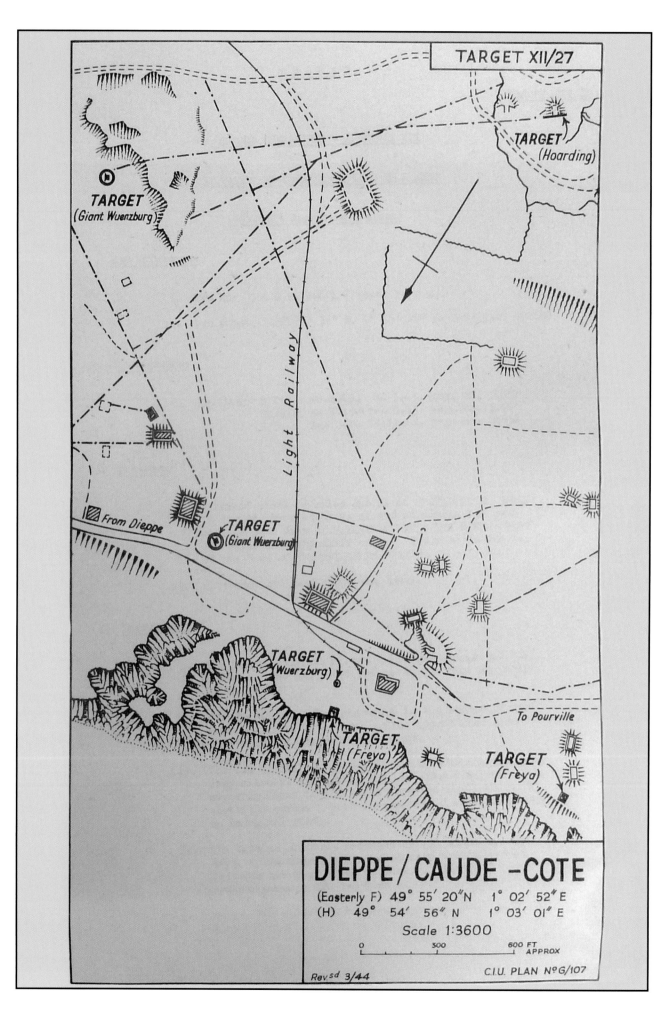

TARGET XII/27

TARGET
(Hoarding)

TARGET
(Giant Wuenzburg)

Light Railway

From Dieppe

TARGET
(Giant Wuerzburg)

TARGET
(Wuerzburg)

To Pourville

TARGET
(Freya)

TARGET
(Freya)

DIEPPE / CAUDE - COTE

(Easterly F) 49° 55′ 20″N   1° 02′ 52″ E
(H)   49° 54′ 56″ N   1° 03′ 01″ E

Scale 1:3600

0   300   600 FT
                              APPROX

Revsd 3/44   C.I.U. PLAN N°G/107

On the landward side of the road are the Hoarding and the two Giant Würzburgs. The Giant nearest the sea is situated on a circular base with a slightly raised rim immediately south of the road at a position 280 yards from pin-point (F). The second Giant is 500 yards further inland on a bearing of 136 degrees true from the first, near a rift in the ground forming a wide trench. There are two sunken buildings close to this instrument.

The Hoarding is situated higher up the slope at pin-point (H), 850 yards inland from the Freyas, and is protected by slit trenches and wire.

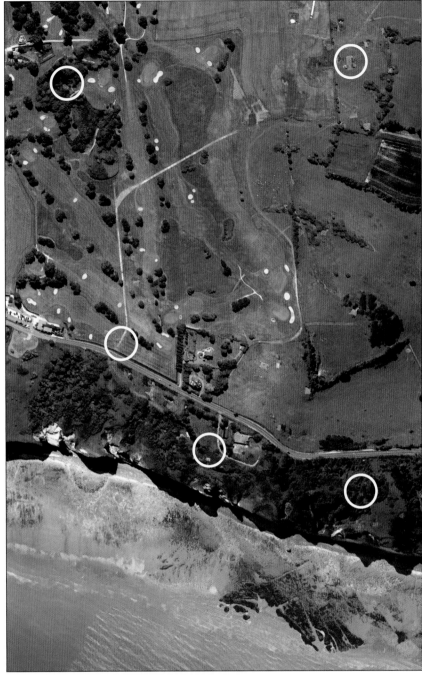

A radar technician, Flight Sergeant Jack Nissenthal, was taken along — much like Cox at Bruneval a few months earlier in the year — to evaluate the Freya and remove any parts that would help develop counter-measures. However, the strength of the German defence prevented the men of the South Saskatchewan Regiment from gaining the position. Two years later, the Dieppe/Caude-Côte site was attacked on June 2, 1944 by rocket-firing Typhoons from Nos. 198 and 609 Squadrons of the Second Tactical Air Force. Eighteen 60lb missiles were fired with claims that the Hoarding had been destroyed and the Würzburgs damaged. The CO of the former unit, Squadron Leader John Niblett, was hit and crashed into the cliffs.

Back in the 1970s, Jacques Collé opened his Musée Militaire de Dieppe at Pourville. The site of the Würzburg near the cliff-top lay in the area included within the grounds of his property.

When he excavated what he thought was the control post (left), he came across various electronic components including valves (right). The museum closed in 1991.

Code-named 'Fliege', the station at Manneville was operated by the 4. Flugmelde-Leit-Kompanie of Luft-Nachrichten-Regiment 53.

ST VALÉRY-EN-CAUX/MANNEVILLE-ÈS-PLAINS

AIRCRAFT REPORTING STATION

Coordinates: 49° 51'55"N 0° 45' 20" E
Grid reference: 992638
Altitude: 250ft

Situated about 1½ miles due east of St Valéry-en-Caux, in fields immediately north of and adjoining the main coastal road from St Valéry to Veule-les-Roses about 700 yards from the cliff edge. The site is due north of the town of Manneville-ès-Plains.

The target consists of two Giant Würzburgs and two Freyas. The pinpoint refers to the more easterly Freya.

The Freyas are 100 yards apart in the centre of the site and close to several sunken operational huts: they stand in square emplacements.

The two Giants are on the east and west sides of the site respectively, and are approximately 400 yards apart. The westerly Giant is 120 yards from the road, the other about 140 yards. Both are on raised sites and stand on hexagonal bases.

The area is strongly defended on all sides by wire defence and mines, and an elaborate trench system protects the most vital points. Individual trench systems protect the two Giants.

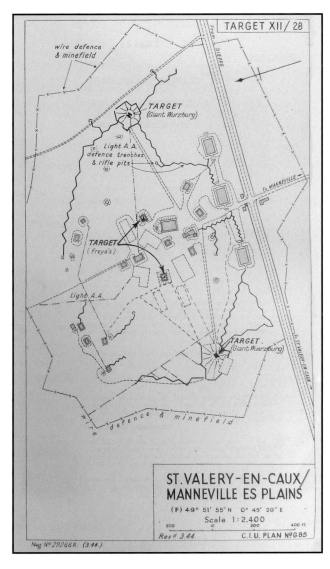

A wind farm now lies in the fields, once the site of Target 28.

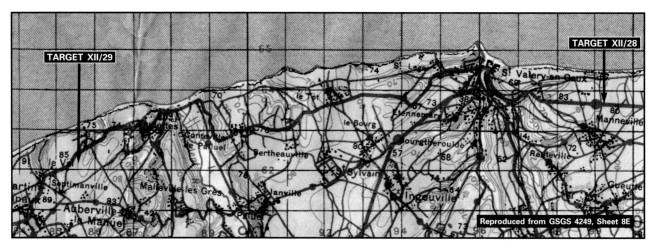

TARGET XII/29

TARGET XII/28

Reproduced from GSGS 4249, Sheet 8E

Describing Target XII/29 as being at St Valéry is somewhat of a misnomer as it lies six miles away west of the town.

ST VALÉRY-EN-CAUX/ST MARTIN-AUX-BUNEAUX

DAY FIGHTER CONTROL STATION

Coordinates: 49° 50'18"N 0° 33' 39" E
Grid reference: 850622
Altitude: 280ft

Six miles west of St Valéry-en-Caux, on the extreme eastern outskirts of the little town of St Martin-aux-Buneaux, situated in open fields between the cliff edge and the coastal road between St Martin and Veulettes. The target is between 500 yards and 700 yards from the cliff edge.

The target consists of two lattice pylons, about 60 feet high, standing 276 yards apart on a bearing of 33 degrees true. The pin-point refers to the more southerly target. The pylons are undefended.

A few fields to the west is a well-defended site in the fields lying directly north of St Martin and occupied by a radio-navigational beam station. This should not be confused with the target.

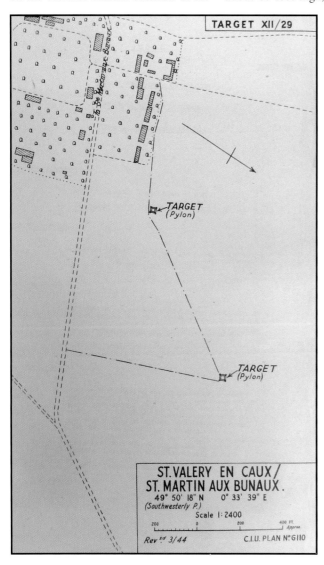

This site was given the code-name 'Dora' by the Germans.

106

Target cover at St Martin-aux-Buneaux taken on January 5, 1944.

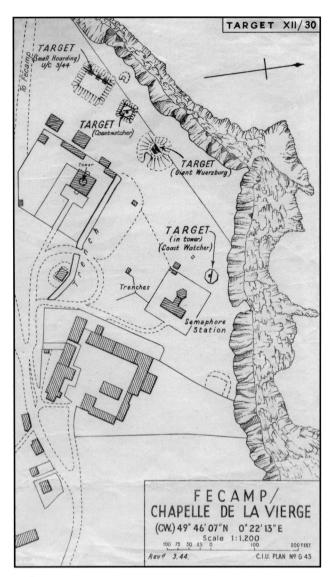

TARGET XII/30

FÉCAMP/
CHAPELLE DE LA VIERGE
(CW.) 49° 46'07"N   0° 22'13" E
Scale 1:1,200
100 75 50 25 0   100   200 FEET
Rev⁴ 3.44.   C.I.U. PLAN N° G 43

FÉCAMP/CHAPELLE DE LA VIERGE

A further nine miles down the coast lay Target XII/30 with a Würzburg, Coastwatchers and a Small Hoarding.

COASTAL SHIP-WATCHING STATION

Coordinates: 49° 46'07"N 0° 22' 13" E
Grid reference: 706557
Altitude: 350ft

Situated on the promontory overlooking the north side of Fécamp harbour, and close to the northern face of the cliffs, in front of the semaphore station at Chapelle de la Vierge, and 500 yards east of the Harbour Bar.

The target consists of two Coastwatchers, a Giant Würzburg and a Small Hoarding. These stand within a few yards of each other a few feet from the cliff edge. The more easterly Coastwatcher to which the pin-point refers, is enclosed within a tall octagonal cylinder. The Giant is on a mounded site, the second Coastwatcher is in a square emplacement partially camouflaged and the Hoarding stands on top of a concrete casemate; in this order from east to west.

Amid the remains of defensive bunkers, the three bases for the Hoarding still stand on the edge of the cliff.

lighthouse   TARGETS

FÉCAMP

Dr Jones, the Assistant Director of Scientific Intelligence, explains that the vital concept of the whole campaign leading up to D-Day was to do everything possible to give the Germans the impression that we were going to land east of the Seine. Dr Jones writes that 'in Operation "Taxable" we aimed at giving the impression that a large sea-borne force was heading in that direction and the invention of the metallic strips called 'Window' was going to make this possible. The Lancasters of No. 617 Squadron were to fly a rectangular orbit, eight miles long by two wide, moving the centre point of each orbit in a south-easterly direction towards Fécamp at eight knots, the speed of a naval convoy. "Window" would be dropped the whole time to create a radar smoke-screen and giving the impression of an invasion force. To work the "spoof" convoy had to be observed by the Germans and, to this end, orders were issued that the radar station at Fécamp (see map page 110) was not to be attacked.'

FECAMP/CHAPELLE DE LA VIERGE   TARGET XII/30
VIEW LOOKING S.W.
ST. LÉONARD
FÉCAMP
TARGETS
ST. BENOIST
SENNEVILLE-SUR-FÉCAMP
42 N°3·26 1·6·42   DUPE NEG. N° 1017

FECAMP/CHAPELLE DE LA VIERGE   TARGET XII/30
ST. BENOIT
ST. NICOLAS
ST. LÉONARD
Heavy & Light A.A.   FÉCAMP
TARGET
ENGLISH   CHANNEL

Jones goes on to say that 'when I visited Thorney Island [the Coastal Command base which had now been allotted to the Second Tactical Air Force], I found the Typhoon pilots consulting the squadron's copy of our "Rhubarb" Appendix (see page 47) and inspecting the wealth of photos covering each target for themselves. They also put forward the names of stations that they would like to attack. Of course the targets were decided on a central plan, not at the request of the pilots, and that in particular Fécamp was not to be attacked. However, on June 3 I was back at Thorney and found the pilots clamouring to be allowed to tackle Fécamp, obviously having been attracted by the detail shown on Target Plan XII/30 (opposite). Although I felt nothing was really necessary to boost their morale, the sense of participation would reward their enthusiasm so I took their request back to headquarters at Stanmore. I argued that since the target had not yet been attacked, at all, its operators were likely to be the least flustered of any in the whole coastal chain, and therefore the most likely to be able to detect that our spoof convoy was false. This argument won the day and, reluctantly, it was agreed to send an order for a small attack to be made. However, when the report came in it was obvious that the pilots had interpreted their orders very liberally, and had given Fécamp everything they could carry. In fact, 28 Typhoons had taken part, firing innumerable cannon shells and 96 60lb rockets, and dropping seven tons of bombs, many of them delayed action.'

View looking E.S.E.

CAP D'ANTIFER/SÉMAPHORE

The radar stations at Cap d'Antifer were listed by the CIU as targets XII/31 and 32. They covered four different sites, one of which being the one of the Bruneval Raid of 1942.

COASTAL SHIP-WATCHING STATION

Coordinates: 49° 41'10"N 0° 09' 55" E
Grid reference: 549481
Altitude: 330ft

Target stands 2½ miles south-west of Étretat in front of the semaphore station, north of Cap d'Antifer, a few yards from the cliff edge, and about 100 yards north-west of the lighthouse.

It consists of a Giant Würzburg and a Coastwatcher, both within the compound of the semaphore station. The Giant stands on a raised earth mound.

The area occupied by the target, the semaphore station and the lighthouse is defended by wire, and there are trenches on the north side as well as one running seaward between the two instruments.

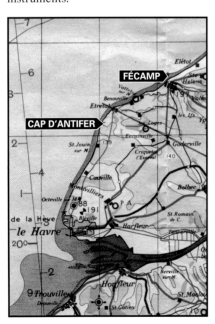

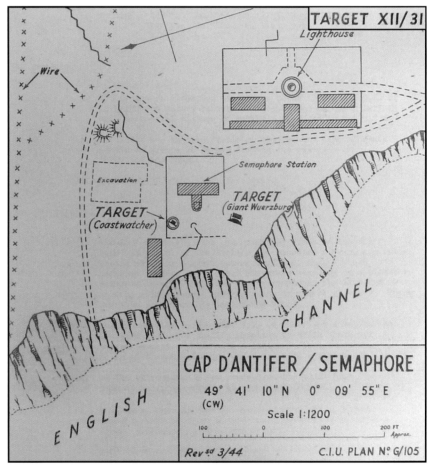

There was no part of the coast of Northern France that was devoid of aircraft reporting or ship-watching radar. (See plan pages 48-49.) The average deployment of the small Würzburgs along the whole of the 450 miles of coastline from the Franco-Belgian frontier to Cap Fréhel in Brittany was one set every 4¼ miles. In the densest, most vulnerable, region between Cap Blanc-Nez and Boulogne there was an average deployment of one set every 1¼ miles, while in an average area such as that between Cayeux and Le Havre it was one set per three miles. At Cap d'Antifer, the most northerly installation was at the semaphore station.

Targets XII/31 and 32 were so close together that the vertical aerial for XII/31 *(above)* also showed the northernmost of the three sites of XII/32. The vertical aerial for the latter *(below)* on the other hand arrowed its five targets but did not indicate those of XII/31. We have put in a white box to indicate the area of the other aerial.

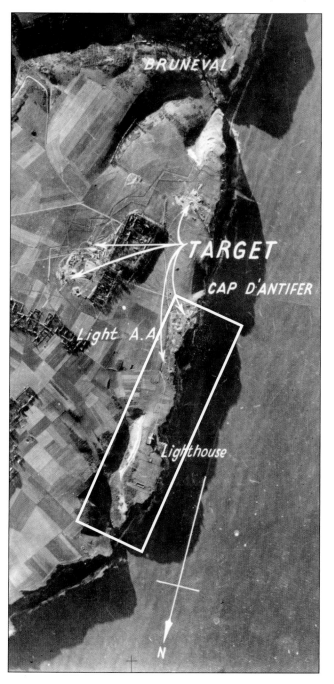

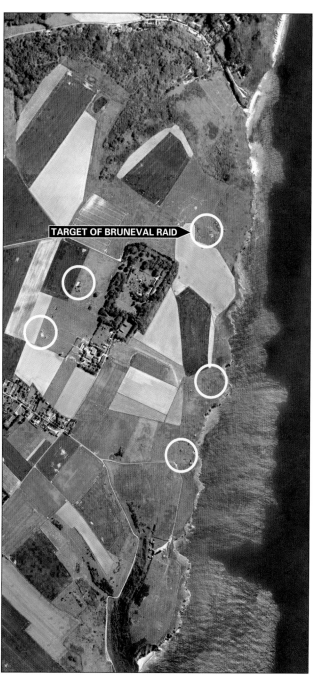

This station — Target XII/32 (code-named by the Germans 'Auerhahn') — was a priority for attack to prevent the landings in Normandy being detected. The Central Interpretation Unit advised on the more vulnerable parts to attack 'as in almost every case the cabin will be the most profitable for, besides the destruction of radio components and operators, the probable damage to turning gear and to the structure generally would involve the enemy in almost complete reconstruction, in some cases in complete replacement. This will hold good for the two types of Freya, the Coastwatcher, the Girder Chimney, the Box Chimney (the cabin halfway up the tower should be a good objective), the Würzburg and Giant Würzburg. Aerial arrays are always exposed and the enemy can do little for their protection, but on the other hand, they are not easy targets, and may not be so readily seen against the background. Furthermore, since most of the arrays rotate, aircraft will have to determine their line of approach at the time of the attack in order to ensure a full broadside view from in front or behind. This complication, however, does not arise with the Hoardings with their fixed orientation.' This is the base of the Würzburg Riese near the cliff-top.

CAP D'ANTIFER

AIRCRAFT REPORTING STATION

Coordinates:
(CH) 49° 40'24"N 0° 09' 45" E
(CH) Grid reference 546467
(F) 49° 40' 45" N 0° 09' 46" E
(F) Grid reference 547473
Altitude: 350ft

The target is dispersed over three sites 13 miles north-north-east of Le Havre and midway between the lighthouse on Cap d'Antifer and the coastal village of Bruneval 1¼ miles to the south-south-west.

The sites are in open fields on the coastal side of small scattered groups of houses forming the villages of Theuville and Jumel.

The most northerly site at pin-point (F) close to the cliff edge, 750 yards south of the lighthouse, contains a Freya apparatus beside a small operational hut. A short distance further south, a Giant Würzburg stands on a circular concrete base. This site is surrounded on the landward side by a long trench outside which is a belt of wire. There are also slit trenches behind the Giant.

The second site is 500 yards south-east of the first site, on the landward side of a small plantation in which there are several houses. This site contains a Giant Würzburg on an earth-mound base, and a Freya in a square emplacement.

On the third site, a few yards from the cliff edge, is Chimney radar apparatus, at pin-point (CH).

The entire area is heavily defended by light AA and a double belt of wire, as well as additional wire defence round individual parts of the target.

On June 4, 23 Spitfires of Nos. 441, 442 and 443 Squadrons dive-bombed Target XII/32 with 500lb bombs fitted with instantaneous fuzes and nine direct hits were claimed. The Chimney (which had been erected on the site of the villa at Bruneval) and one Giant Würzburg and other installations were damaged. These are the foundations of the Freya.

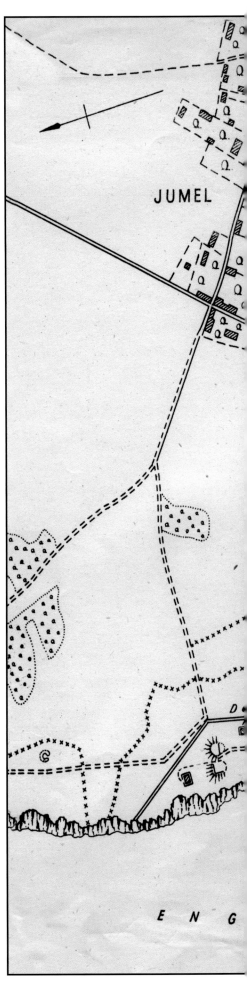

JUMEL

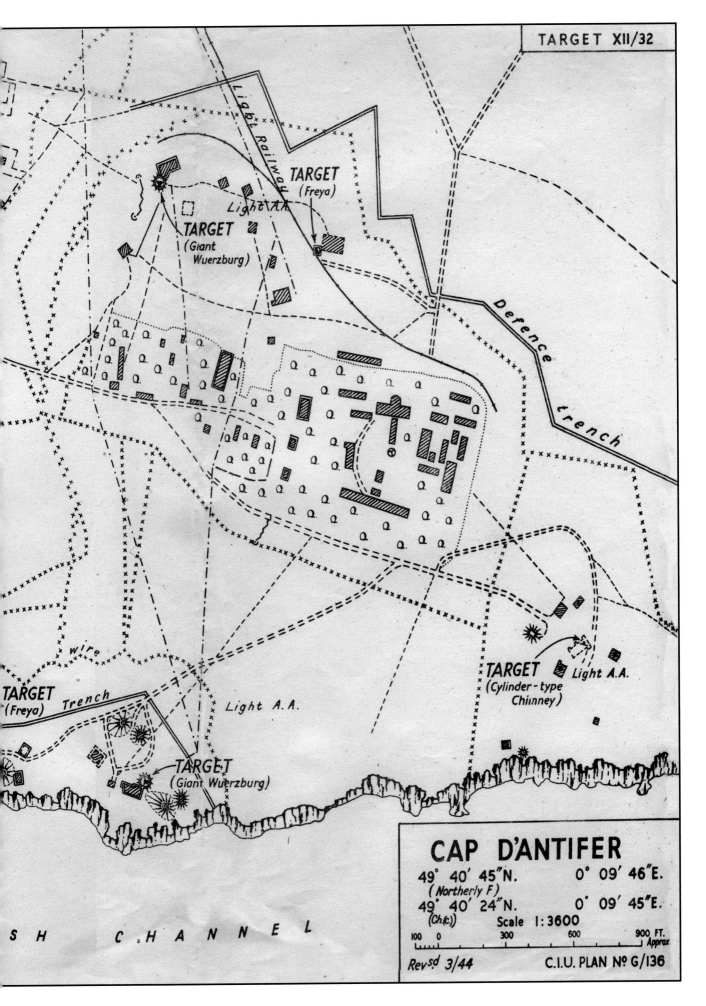

TARGET XII/32

TARGET
(Freya)

Light A.A.

TARGET
(Giant
Wuerzburg)

Light Railway

Defence trench

wire

TARGET
(Freya)   Trench

Light A.A.

TARGET
(Cylinder-type
Chimney)   Light A.A.

TARGET
(Giant Wuerzburg)

SH   CHANNEL

CAP D'ANTIFER
49° 40′ 45″N.   0° 09′ 46″E.
(Northerly F)
49° 40′ 24″N.   0° 09′ 45″E.
(Ch.c.)   Scale 1:3600
100   0   300   600   900 FT.
                                        Approx.
Rev.sd 3/44   C.I.U. PLAN No G/136

113

JUMEL

TARGET

Light A.A.

TARGET

TARGET

Taken on April 4, 1943, just over a year after the raid on Bruneval, work is underway on the villa site (below left). By this time, the Würzburg was being replaced by a Cylinder-type Chimney (Wassermann). (See also pages 35-36.)

114

In the Cap d'Antifer briefing notes, the Central Interpretation Unit warned that 'the entire area is heavily defended by light AA' and on May 11 the Typhoons of No. 609 Squadron were the third unit to go into the attack only to be greeted by defences that were fully alert. Two aircraft were hit, Flight Lieutenant Robert Wood going down in flames. He is now remembered on the Runnymede Memorial to the Missing.

Retired Dutch army officer Lenco van der Weel and photographer Arthur van Beveren have had an abiding passion for seeking out and recording German fortifications. Their website (*www.bunkersite.com*) is a mine of information, not only on the Atlantic Wall but many other locations in Europe. Much of the site at Cap d'Antifer remains open to be visited and explored. This was the entrance gate to the Flak battery.

One of the ammunition bunkers within site of the lighthouse at the neighbouring Target XII/31.

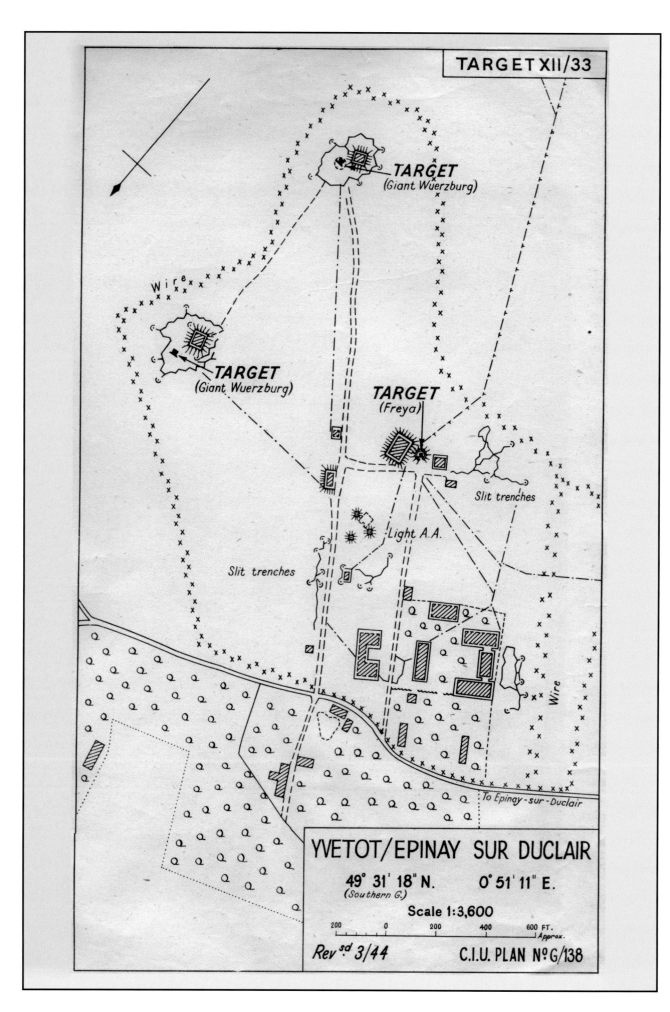

TARGET XII/33

TARGET
(Giant Wuerzburg)

Wire

TARGET
(Giant Wuerzburg)

TARGET
(Freya)

Slit trenches

Light A.A.

Slit trenches

Wire

To Epinay-sur-Duclair

YVETOT/EPINAY SUR DUCLAIR

49° 31′ 18″ N.   0° 51′ 11″ E.
(Southern G.)

Scale 1:3,600

200   0   200   400   600 FT.
Approx.

Rev.sd 3/44   C.I.U. PLAN Nº G/138

116

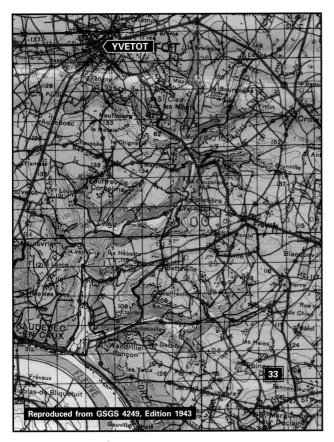

Reproduced from GSGS 4249, Edition 1943

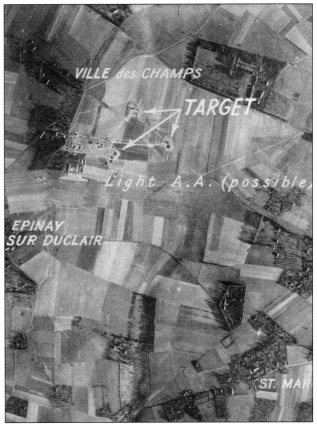

YVETOT/ÉPINAY-SUR-DUCLAIR

Target XII/33, comprising a Freya and two Giant Würzburgs, lay 25 miles inland from the coast. *Below:* Little to be seen today in the fields at Épinay-sur-Duclair.

GROUND CONTROL INTERCEPTION STATION

Coordinates: 49° 31'18"N 0° 51' 11" E
Grid reference: 027251
Altitude: 350ft

The station is seven miles south-east of Yvetot and five miles east of Caude-bec-en-Caux on the River Seine on high ground in open fields three quarters of a mile east of the village of Épinay-sur-Duclair.

The target lies 25 miles from the coast and consists of a Freya apparatus and two Giant Würzburgs. The pin-point refers to the southerly Giant.

The second Giant is situated 308 yards to the north of the pin-point, and the Freya is 420 yards away on a bearing of 304 degrees true.

The site was defended by a battery of 20mm Flak guns and the station was manned by the 20. Flugmelde-Leit-Kompanie of Luft-Nachrichten-Regiment 53. The CIU commented that 'the Freya [FuMG 450] remained the commonest instrument of detection for aircraft' and that the introduction of the Giant Würzburg [FuSE 65] 'had extended the range for height-finding from 25 miles to about 40 miles'. A warning was given that 'shipping approaching any part of the coasts of Northern France is liable to detection at ranges up to 25 miles, and further than this in conditions of anomalous propagation which occur frequently in Summer'.

NEUFCHÂTEL/SULLY

GROUND CONTROL INTERCEPTION STATION

Coordinates: 49° 32'55"N 1° 45' 47" E
Grid reference: 685225
Altitude: 700ft

This site is 54 miles north-north-west of Paris, 39 miles from Dieppe, and 10½ miles south-east of Forges, between and slightly to the south of the villages of Bazancourt and Sully. The target stands on commanding ground on one of the highest points of the undulating country lying between two railways running south-eastwards, viz. the main line from Serqueux to Gournay-en-Bray and the narrow gauge line from Formerie to Songeons.

The target consists of two Giant Würzburgs and a Freya, the above pin-point referring to the southerly Giant. The second Giant is situated 245 yards away on a bearing of 345 degrees true. The Freya, in a circular emplacement, stands 400 yards from the pin-point on a bearing of 290 degrees true. The central part of the site is occupied by several long sunken huts.

The southerly Giant is protected by fire trenches almost encircling it. Both Giants are surrounded by a very wide belt of wire defence. The Freya and adjacent huts are enclosed by two irregular heavy belts of wire.

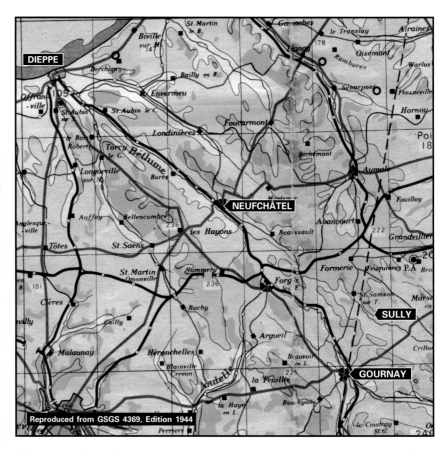

Although positioned inland, the commanding location of the Sully site on top of high ground 700 feet above sea level, gave this intercept station a perfect second line of defence. (Although called Neufchâtel, this station is actually closer to Gournay.)

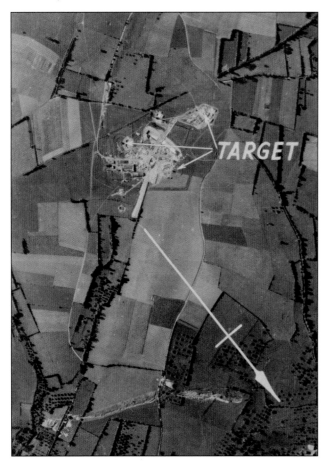

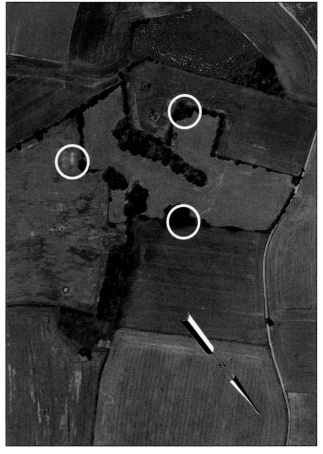

Photo taken of Target XII/34 in October 1943 when in was still under construction. The unit that manned the station (code-named 'Biene') was the 17. Flugmelde-Leit-Kompanie of Luft-Nachrichten-Regiment 53. The three targets are circled.

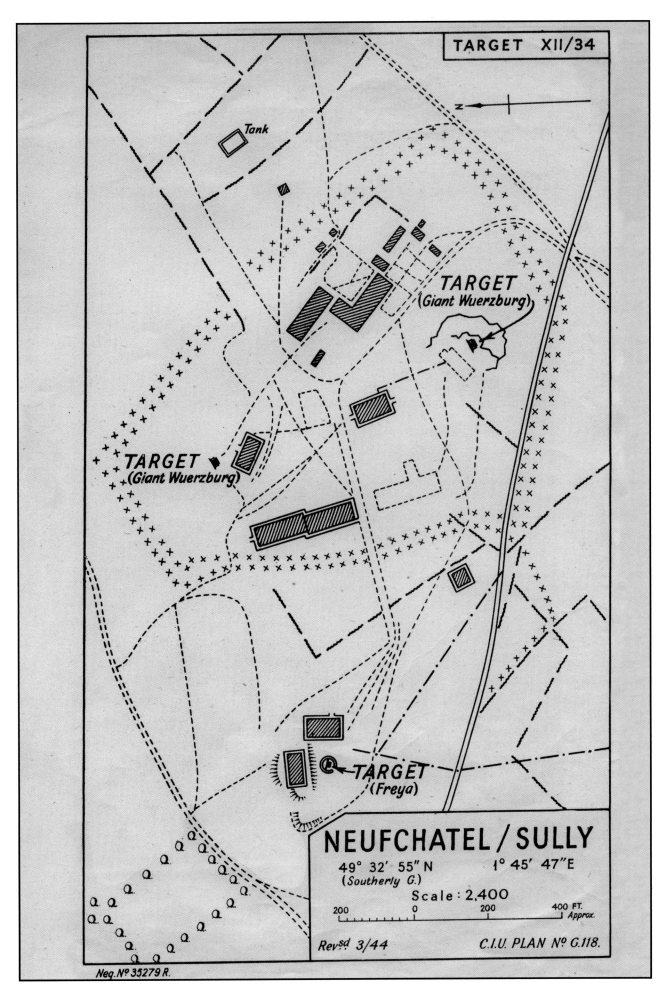

TARGET XII/34

Tank

TARGET
(Giant Wuerzburg)

TARGET
(Giant Wuerzburg)

TARGET
(Freya)

NEUFCHATEL / SULLY

49° 32′ 55″ N   1° 45′ 47″ E
(Southerly G.)

Scale: 2,400

200   0   200   400 FT.
Approx.

Rev*sd* 3/44   C.I.U. PLAN Nº G.118.

Neg.Nº 35279 R.

119

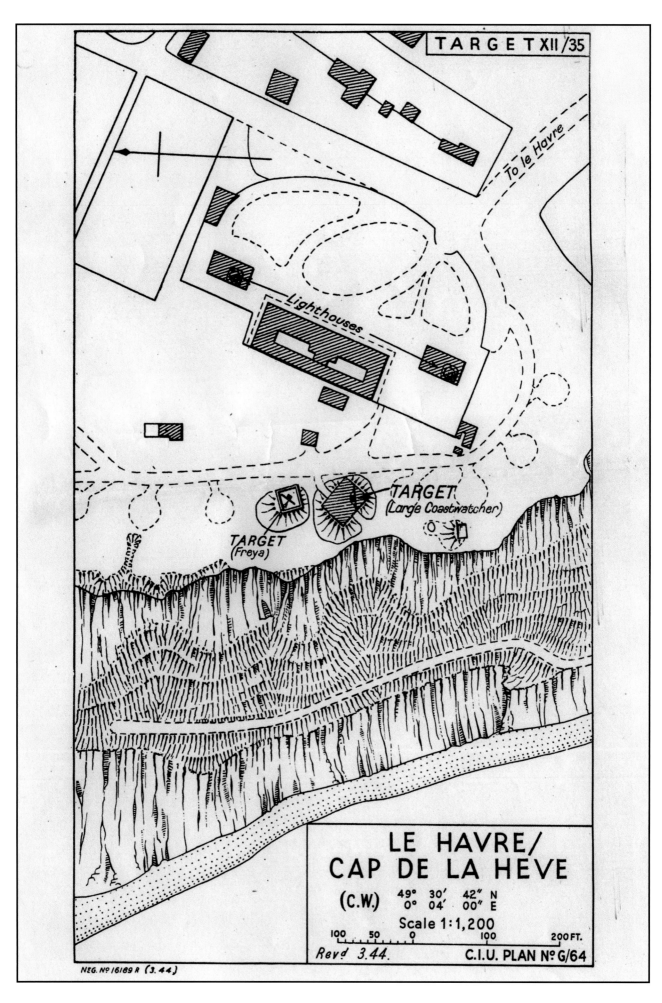

TARGET XII/35

To le Havre

Lighthouses

TARGET
(Large Coastwatcher)

TARGET
(Freya)

LE HAVRE/
CAP DE LA HEVE

(C.W.)   49° 30′ 42″ N
          0° 04′ 00″ E

Scale 1:1,200

100   50   0   100   200 FT.

Revd 3.44.   C.I.U. PLAN Nº G/64

NEG. Nº 16189 R (3.44)

LE HAVRE/CAP DE LA HÈVE

Target XII/35 (code-name 'Gertrud') photographed on June 17, 1942. The area was almost totally destroyed in the bombing that preceeded the battle for Le Havre. (See also page 15.)

COASTAL SHIP-WATCHING STATION

Coordinates: 49° 30'42"N 0° 04' 00" E
Grid reference: 459296
Altitude: 340ft

Situated about 2¼ miles north-west of

the harbour at Le Havre near the old semaphore station on Cap de la Hève, in the area directly in front of, and between, the two lighthouses.

The target consists of a Large Coastwatcher with a square frame aerial 35 feet wide, stainding on the south

corner of a square concrete building, and a Freya situated a few yards north of the large Coastwatcher. (Later a Giant Würzburg was added.)

The whole area is well defended by wire and light AA slit trenches protect the target on the landward side.

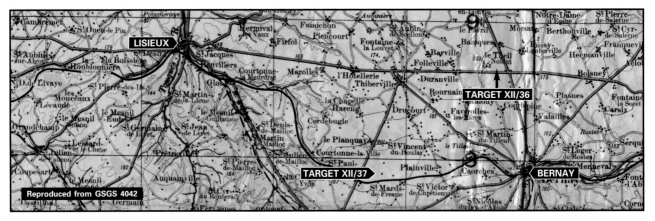

LISIEUX/LE THEIL-NOLENT

At Le Thiel-Nolent, east of Lisieux, Target XII/36 comprised two Giant Würzburgs and a Freya, similar to that illustrated below. We have circled the three targets.

GROUND CONTROL INTERCEPTION STATION

Coordinates: 49° 09'41"N 0° 32' 52" E
Grid reference: 768874
Altitude: 600ft

This target is 14 miles east of Lisieux, just north-east of the village of Le Theil-Nolent and north of the main road to Évreux. It is situated on high ground of fields interspersed by clusters of small woods.

The target consists of two Giant Würzburgs and a Freya apparatus of pole type, to which the pin-point refers. The first Giant is situated 400 yards north-west of the pin-point and on the edge of the area. The second Giant is 200 yards north-north-east of the pin-point, and stands on a circular concrete base surrounded by a trench. The Freya stands in a circular emplacement raised in a concrete mound to a conspicuous height.

The area is heavily defended by elaborate trench systems protecting the Freya and the second Giant, as well as light AA and machine guns. Wire defence surrounds the whole area; on the north side it is of triple depth.

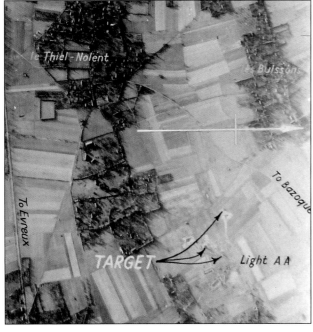

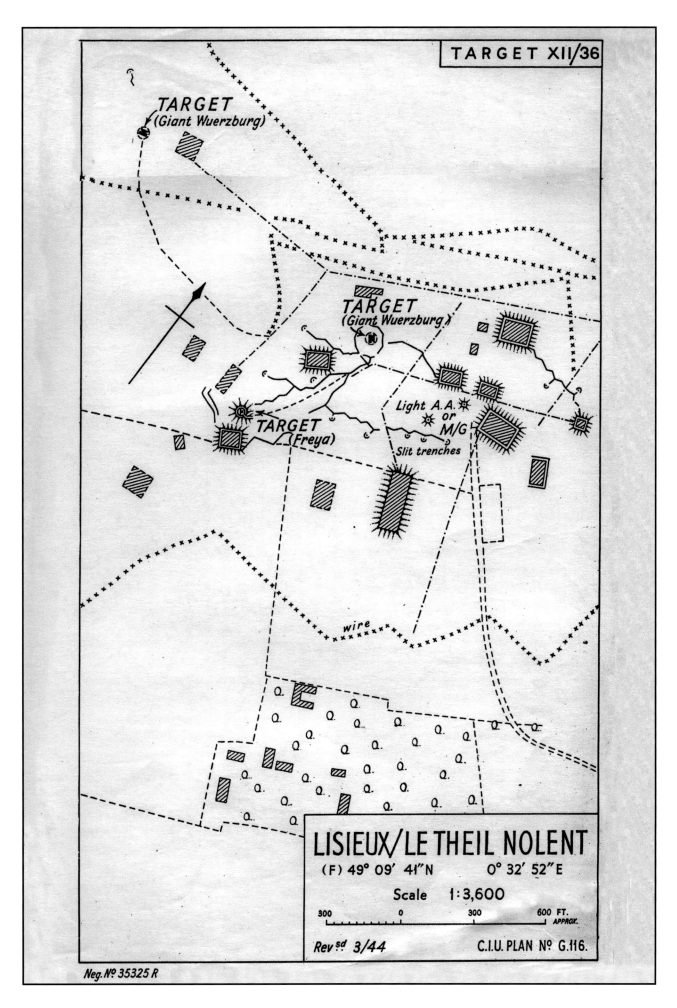

TARGET XII/36

TARGET
(Giant Wuerzburg)

TARGET
(Giant Wuerzburg)

Light A.A.
or
M/G

TARGET
(Freya)

Slit trenches

wire

LISIEUX/LE THEIL NOLENT

(F) 49° 09′ 41″N   0° 32′ 52″E

Scale   1:3,600

300   0   300   600 FT.
APPROX.

Rev.sd 3/44   C.I.U. PLAN Nº G.116.

Neg. Nº 35325 R

123

Just seven miles to the south-west of Le Theil-Nolent (see map page 122) lay the day fighter control station at La Chalière: CIU's Target XII/37. The Germans code-named it 'Baumläufer' and it was manned by the 7. Flugmelde-Leit-Kompanie of Luft-Nachrichten-Regiment 53.

BERNAY/LA CHALIÈRE

DAY FIGHTER CONTROL STATION

Coordinates: 49° 05'00"N 0° 27' 00" E
Grid reference: 689795
Altitude: 620ft

This site lays 4¾ miles north-north-east of Orbec and seven miles west of Bernay, in fields just east of the little hamlet of La Chalière, ¾ of a mile north of the railway between Bernay and Lisieux.

The target consists of five receiver pylons and five transmitter huts to each of which is attached a slender mast. The height of the receiver pylons is about 60 feet, the transmitter masts 80 feet. The area occupied by the installation covers 620 yards north to south by 520 yards east to west. The pylons are placed regularly in two lines approximately 270 yards apart. The disposition of the transmitters is irregular, each hut being about 100 yards from the next.

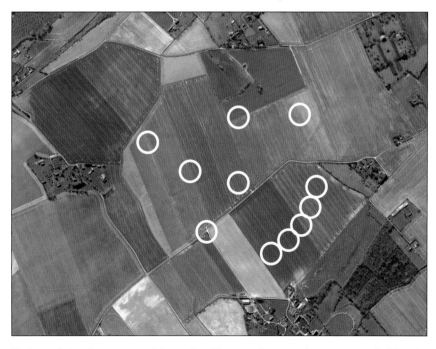

Both roads leading eastward from the village, and across the area occupied by the target (over 60 acres), were defended by slit trenches.

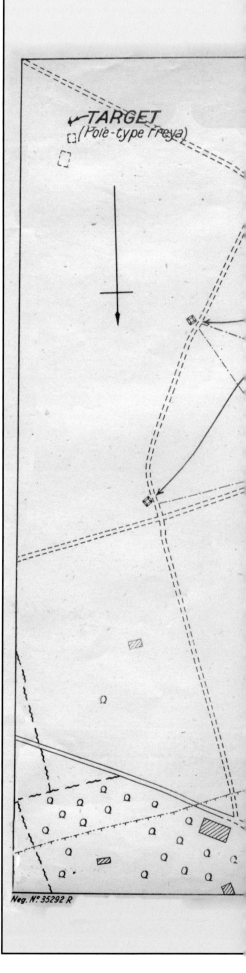

TARGET
(Pole-type Freya)

Neg. N° 35292 R

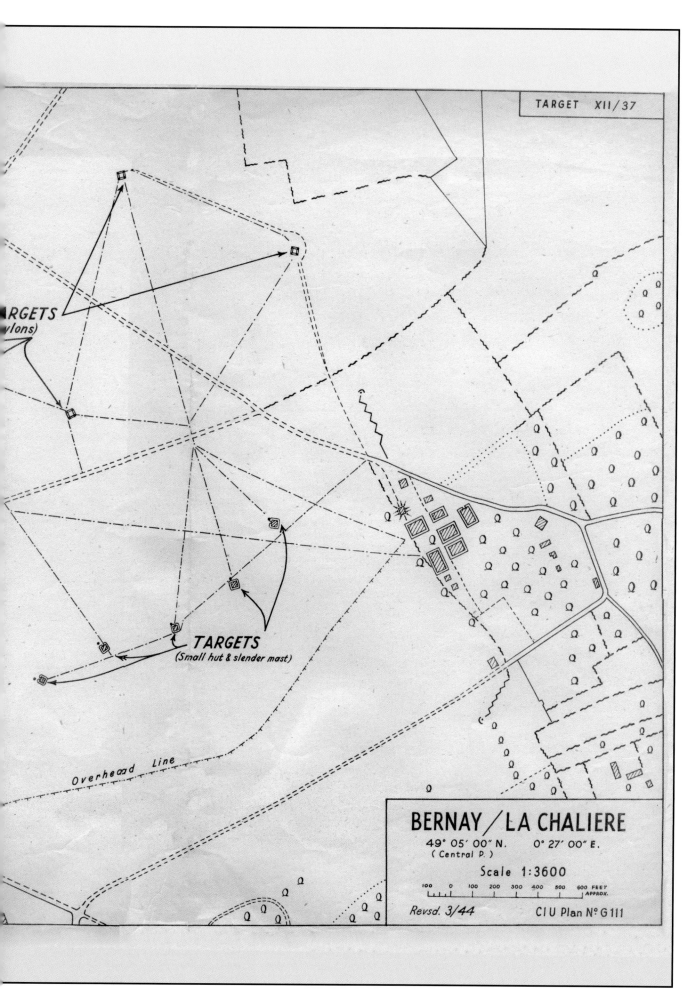

ARGETS
ylons)

TARGETS
(Small hut & slender mast)

Overhead Line

BERNAY / LA CHALIERE
49° 05′ 00″ N.   0° 27′ 00″ E.
(Central P.)

Scale 1:3600

100   0   100   200   300   400   500   600 FEET
                                              APPROX.

Revsd. 3/44   CIU Plan N° G 111

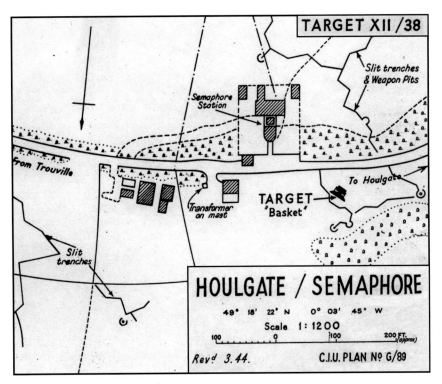

TARGET XII/38

Slit trenches & Weapon Pits

Semaphore Station

From Trouville

To Houlgate

TARGET "Basket"

Transformer on mast

Slit trenches

HOULGATE / SEMAPHORE

49° 18' 22" N   0° 03' 45" W

Scale 1:1200

100   0   100   200 FT. (approx)

Rev⁴ 3.44.   C.I.U. PLAN № G/89

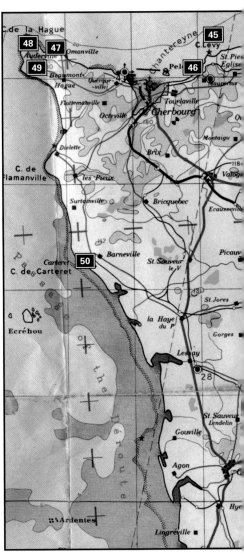

HOULGATE/SÉMAPHORE

COASTAL SHIP-WATCHING STATION

Coordinates: 49° 18'22"N 0° 03' 45" W
Grid reference: 255812
Altitude: 375ft

Target XII/38 is seven miles west-south-west of Deauville and close to the coast in front of the semaphore station, ½ a mile east-north-east of the town.

The target is on the seaward side of the road running along the coast between the semaphore station and the cliff edge, at a slightly lower level than the former.

The target consists of a single Giant Würzburg used as a Coastwatcher and set on a rough earth mound.

There are slit trenches and weapon pits slightly to the west of the target.

Now we are approaching the invasion area, we must remember the criteria laid down in the 'Overlord' planning to prevent the chain of radar stations detecting or identifying the area chosen for the landings.

There were two alternatives: direct air attack or jamming, and on May 15 an advisory staff for SHAEF Radio Counter-Measures was set up under Air Vice-Marshal Victor Tait, the Director General of Signals, to make the necessary selections. However, to avoid disclosing the precise location for the landings, two sites outside the chosen area were attacked for every one within it. Also it was considered unwise to commence the campaign of radar air attacks too soon as it would then give the German engineers time to repair the damage. Attacks began on May 10 against the long-range Aircraft Reporting Stations as it was considered they would be difficult to repair quickly. Also they would be difficult to jam as they operated with a very narrow beam. A week later the targets switched to Fighter Control Stations and those used for gun-laying by coastal batteries. Then, in the week before the invasion, intensive attacks were to take place on 42 chosen sites. Most of the attacks were made by rocket-firing Typhoons and during the period they flew 694 sorties, firing 4,517 rockets. At the same time, bomb-carrying Spitfires carried out 759 sorties, dropping 1,258 bombs. Targets were subjected to strafing from cannons and machine guns at low-level which inevitably led to heavy losses.

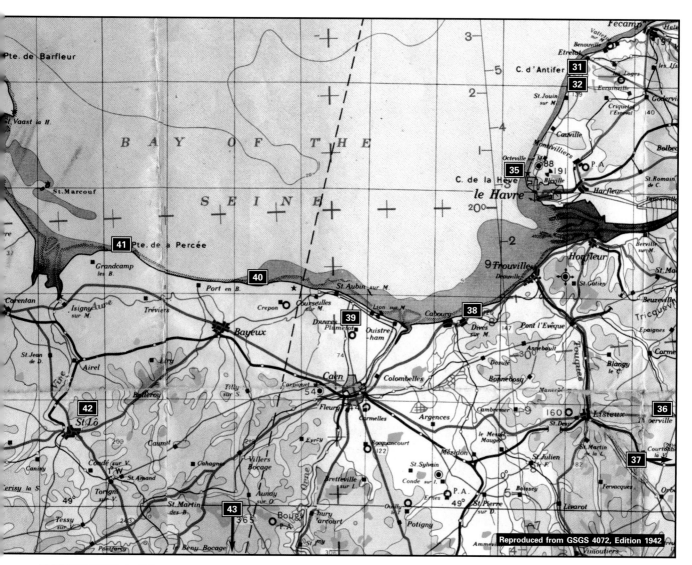

On May 3, 1944, King George VI visited Northolt to inspect examples of the latest RAF types and the armaments that were to be used in the invasion. This Typhoon of No. 183 Squadron had been brought up specially from its base at Thorney Island, Hampshire, by its pilot, Squadron Leader, the Hon. Felix Scarlett. Just eight days after this picture was taken, Scarlett would have a lucky escape when hit by Flak while attacking the radar station at Cap d'Antifer (page 112). The starboard fuel tank caught fire so he jettisoned the hood preparing to bale out when the flames went out so he was able to return to Thorney Island. However, after repair, the aircraft (MN454) was issued to No. 164 Squadron only to be shot down by a Focke-Wulf 190 on D-Day, Flying Officer Alfred Roberts from Victoria, Australia, being killed. The worst day for Typhoon losses was May 24 when five were shot down and five more damaged, with four of the pilots

killed, one wounded and one captured. Also, when No. 198 Squadron attacked the station at Jobourg on the Cap de la Hague (see page 155), they lost two pilots. A German soldier later told his interrogators what happened. Three Typhoons came in flying very low. The second aircraft [Flying Officer Harold Freeman] received a direct hit from 37mm Flak that practically shot off its tail. He somehow managed to keep control and fire his rockets and then tried to clear the target. The following Typhoon [Pilot Officer Edward Vallely] attempted to avoid Freeman but touched his fuselage and both aircraft crashed into the installation. The soldier said that he believed that Freeman had deliberately crashed his aircraft into the target. When this became known to the squadron, his name was put forward for the award of a posthumous Victoria Cross but this was turned down. Instead he received just a Mention in Despatches.

CAEN/DOUVRES-LA-DÉLIVRANDE

EARLY WARNING STATION

Coordinates: 49° 17'13"N 0° 24' 24" W
Grid reference: 004800
Altitude: 200ft

Situated on high ground, three miles inland from St Aubin-sur-Mer and one mile north-east of the village of Basly. Station consists of two Freyas and two 'Basket' RDF apparatus on a well laid-out site, divided unequally in two by the minor road from Douvres to Basly. The four instruments are widely spaced on the northern side, and the majority of the station buildings closely grouped on the other side of the road.

Each Freya apparatus stands in a built-up and camouflaged emplacement, semi-circular in shape, while the 'Baskets' are unemplaced upon a concrete base.

Many shelters and defence trenches are under construction and at least one light AA battery of three guns is within the double belt of wire which surrounds the station. In between the two belts of wire is a minefield.

Apart from being a critical radar station, Douvres-la-Délivrande — Target XII/39 — was also a formidable strong point, named 'Distelfink' by the Germans. Situated within the Canadian sector behind Juno Beach, it comprised two compounds on either side of the Douvres-Basly road. In addition to the Wassermann FuMG 42 Siemens latticework tower, the main site had two FuSE 65 Würzburg Riese (labelled as 'Baskets' by the CIU on the plan opposite) and two FuMG 80 Freyas. The whole complex was protected by a range of armaments including 20mm cannon, 5cm anti-tank guns and a 5cm field piece, manned by a garrison of over 200 Luftwaffe personnel. The 20-acre site also lay within a minefield and a ring of barbed wire some 20 feet thick.

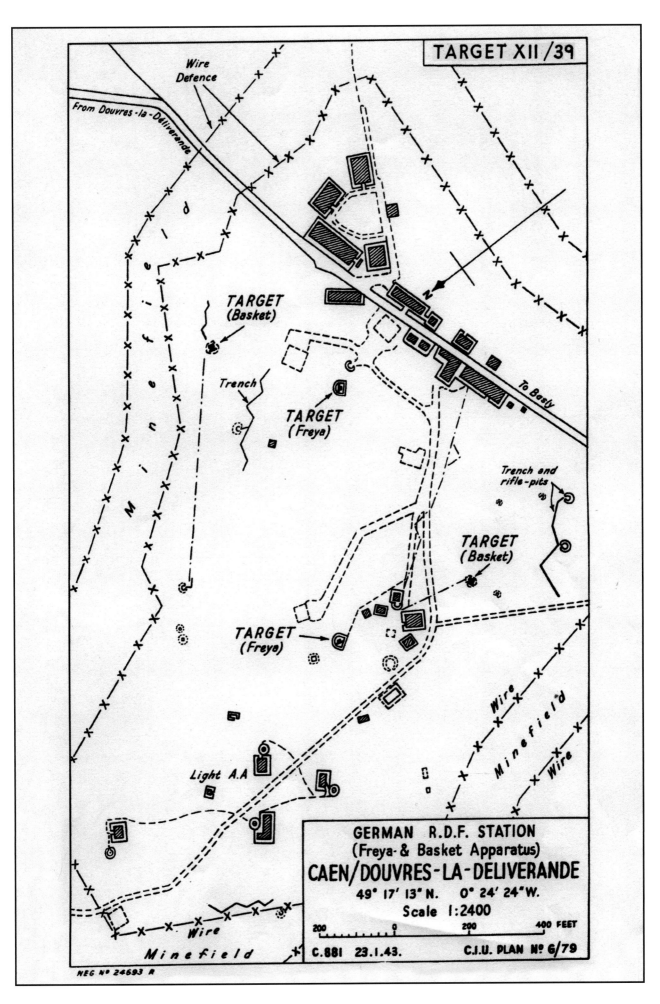

TARGET XII/39

Wire Defence

From Douvres-la-Délivérande

Minefield

TARGET (Basket)

Trench

TARGET (Freya)

N

To Basly

Trench and rifle-pits

TARGET (Basket)

TARGET (Freya)

Wire

Minefield

Wire

Light A.A

GERMAN R.D.F. STATION
(Freya-& Basket Apparatus)
CAEN/DOUVRES-LA-DÉLIVERANDE
49° 17' 13" N.   0° 24' 24" W.
Scale 1:2400

200   0   200   400 FEET

C.881   23.1.43.   C.I.U. PLAN Nº 6/79

Wire

Minefield

NEG Nº 24693 R

129

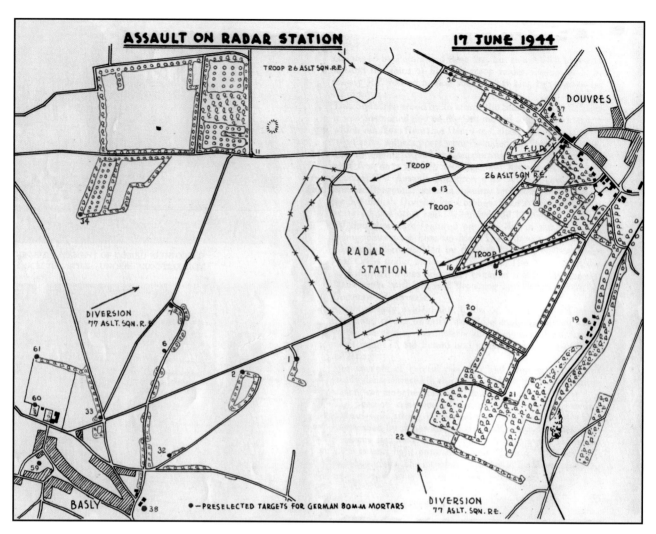

ASSAULT ON RADAR STATION   17 JUNE 1944

The 3rd Canadian Infantry Division isolated the station but it remained a thorn in their side for 12 days. Although naval shelling destroyed the main antenna, an attempt by infantry to capture the site had to be discontinued due to mounting casualties. Instead Douvres was bypassed while being mortared, shelled and pounded by rockets from Typhoons. Isolated within the bridgehead, on June 17 the final assault went in after a bombardment from 7.2-inch howitzers of the Royal Artillery and Royal Navy ships offshore. After 30 minutes of continual shelling, No. 41 Commando, with the support of over 40 specialised fighting vehicles from the 79th Armoured Division, attacked from the north, while other tanks created a diversion from the south-west.

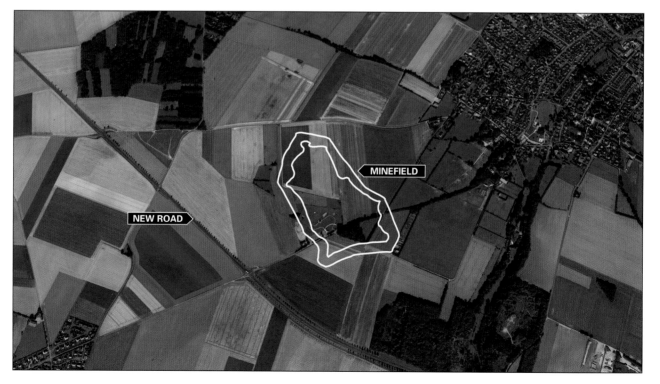

The 79th Armoured Division history explains that the final attack on the radar station was launched on the June 17. 'An assault force of No. 26 Assault Squadron, RE, and B Squadron, 22nd Dragoons, was supported by Royal Marine Commandos. Diversions and covering troops were found by No. 77 Assault Squadron, RE, and operated from the south and west. After an initial bombardment from heavy artillery, four assault teams, each with two mine-clearing 'Crabs' and one troop AVREs, attacked under covering fire from the remaining Crabs. The Crabs flailed, AVREs Petarded shelters and emplacements, dismounted crews placed 70lb 'Beehive' charges under smoke protection, the infantry went in and the garrison surrendered. The 22nd Dragoons lost four or five Crabs on mines; these were all recoverable and no personnel casualties suffered. The 5th Assault Regiment had four AVREs written off and three more damaged by mines; three other ranks were killed and seven wounded. The infantry had no serious casualties.'

Report by the Supreme Commander to the Combined Chiefs-of-Staff, 1946: 'In the British-Canadian sector, chief interest centred in the thrust by the British 3rd and Canadian 3rd Divisions toward Caen. Exploiting the success achieved on D-Day, they pushed southward and succeeded on June 7 in reaching points some two or three miles north and north-west of the city. However, the enemy, employing the tanks of 21st Panzer and 12th SS Panzer Divisions, counter-attacked and penetrated nearly to the coast. Subsequent events showed that the retention of the city was the key to the main enemy strategy and, during the following weeks, the Germans fought furiously to deny us possession. Meanwhile, the Allies had their first experience of the enemy's skill in holding out in fortified strong points behind our lines. Although German claims of the effects of these strong points in delaying the development of our operations were greatly exaggerated, it was undeniably difficult to eliminate the suicide squads by whom they were held. The biggest of these points was at Douvres in the Canadian sector, where the underground installations extended to 300 [sic] feet below the surface, it was not until June 17 that the garrison here was compelled to surrender.'

Surprisingly little damage had resulted from the pre-D-Day attacks, and up to June 6 only one barrack building had been burned out. The radar installations themselves, protected by concrete, were practically undamaged. The RP attacks were particularly ineffective, but the machine-gun fire into the radar cabins was feared and effective, and eight men had been killed prior to D-Day. Apart from short intervals spent repairing cables and an aerial severed by MG fire, the installations were kept continually in operation. On the night of June 6/7, the radar personnel had been busily employed monitoring Allied shipping and at 0100 hours, the Würzburg plotted around 100 ships, the information being passed to Jafü [Jagdführer] 5. The Würzburg and Freya were kept operating even through the later artillery and tank attacks, and it was only when capture became imminent that all the technical apparatus was destroyed by explosive charges. The garrison put up a spirited defence and not until Allied tanks broke through the minefields did the station finally surrender.

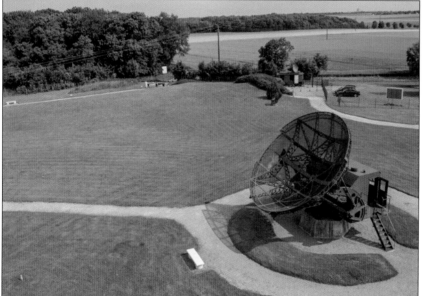

Robert Barr, BBC, June 17, 1944: 'There is still one German strong point which is holding out within six miles of the Normandy coast and many miles behind our front line. The Navy have had a try at smashing it. The Air Force had a try but still the German, garrison held out. We've called off all big-scale attempts to clear it up because the commander in the area has ruled that no heavy casualties must be risked in smashing it. But the point is that this strong point of the West Wall which the Canadians swept past on the first day is still intact. All you can see of it is ordinary fields, with a few grass mounds here and there indicating defence points. You can see a concrete tower hidden amongst trees, and through binoculars you can see the signs: "Achtung. Minen", Beware of Mines. This is a sample of what the Germans hoped to prepare for us along the coast. We've surrounded it, we've shelled it, we've bombed it, and it's still unopened.'

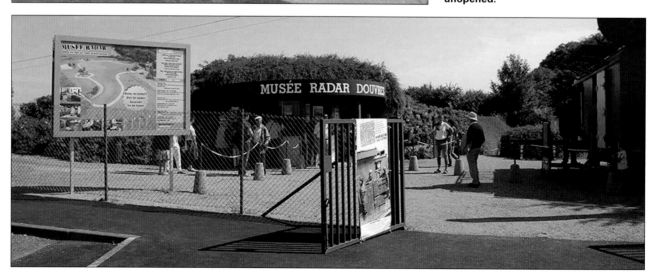

Fifty years later, part of the former Target XII/39 was resurrected by the Caen Memorial and inaugurated on June 5, 1994. Further excavation work was carried out and now, with the addition of a Giant Würzburg obtained from the Observatoire de Paris, it stands as a unique museum to the enemy radar sites in France. (See also Postscript on pages 182-185.)

Frank Gillard, BBC, June 18, 1944: 'You have heard of that colossal strong point just along the coast at Douvres where getting on for 200 Germans held out till last night. That's a place to see. Somebody this morning called it an inverted skyscraper. That's not an unreasonable description. Fifty feet and more into the ground it goes — four stories deep. On the surface you barely notice it. The top's almost flush with the ground. But going down those narrow concrete stairways you think of going into the vaults of the Bank of England. And the Germans did themselves well down below there — central heating, electric light, hot water, air conditioning, radios, telephones, comfortable well-furnished rooms and offices, well- equipped workshops, and ample supplies of food and of ammunition. The Germans who were standing here on this ground 14 days ago certainly must have thought that they had little to fear, and yet what a change now!'

ARROMANCHES

COASTAL SHIP-WATCHING STATION

Coordinates: 49° 20'25"N 0° 36' 57" W
Grid reference: 854865
Altitude: 200ft

This station is 15½ miles north-west of Caen, situated in fields immediately east of the little seaside town of Arromanches. The target stands approximately 30 yards from the cliff edge.

It consists of a Giant Würzburg and a Coastwatcher situated about 30 yards apart. The Giant stands on a hexagonal base set in a slightly sunk concrete emplacement. The Coastwatcher is in a slightly deeper emplacement surrounded by a low wall.

A small tower and two slender wireless telegraphy masts, about 75 feet high, stand about 135 yards to the south-west of the target.

The site is protected on the landward side by a double belt of wire defence. On the side nearest Arromanches are light AA positions.

Several sunken huts adjoin the targets; some of these huts are between the two belts of wire.

The plan for Operation 'Overlord', on D-Day, was to capture the Giant Würzburg on the eastern headland overlooking Arromanches. It was believed the radar would only be lightly held by the station personnel plus a few infantry. Troops were particularly ordered to preserve the equipment from damage, as its examination would be followed up by No. 30 Assault Unit which was a joint services commando unit specially set up and trained in the seizure of intelligence objectives and placed under the direct operational control of the Allied Naval Commander. Arromanches itself had been bombarded by HMS *Scylla* which fired 40 rounds between 0924 and 0931, and later by the guns of the 147th Field Regiment, RA. The town was finally clear by 2100 and the position captured with some 40 prisoners.

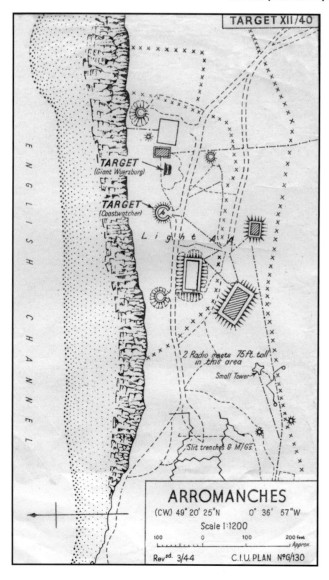

The circles mark the two targets. (See also rear cover.)

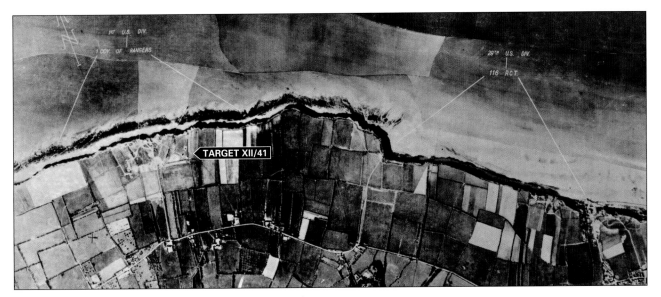

POINTE ET RAZ DE LA PERCÉE

Picture taken on April 27, 1944, with the original annotations added to show the planned touchdown areas for the Rangers (on the left) and the 116th Regiment of the US 29th Division on the right.

COASTAL SHIP-WATCHING STATION

Coordinates: 49° 23'37"N 0° 56' 20" W
Grid reference: 623934
Altitude: 100ft

Target is nine miles north-east of Isigny and dispersed in the area around the semaphore station close to the coast just west of Pointe et Raz de la Percée. It consists of two Giant Würzburgs, a Coastwatcher, and a Pole-type Freya. The pin-point refers to the Coastwatcher, which is sited 100 yards west of the semaphore station in a square concrete emplacement. (See also page 14.)

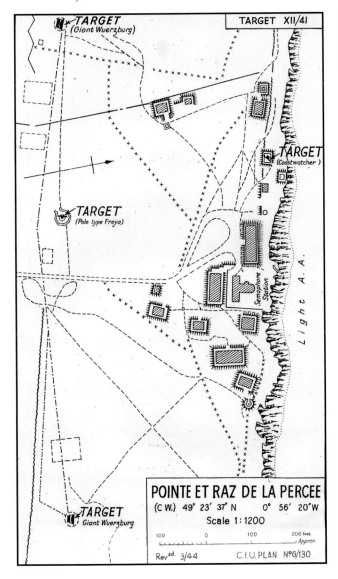

Ther German code-name for the site was 'Ime' and it was operated by the 9. Flugmelde-Leit-Kompanie of Luft-Nachrichten-Regiment 53.

The radar site with its anti-aircraft weaponry was the objective of Company C of the 2nd Ranger Battalion which was to land at the extreme western end of the 29th Division beach and attack it from the landward side.

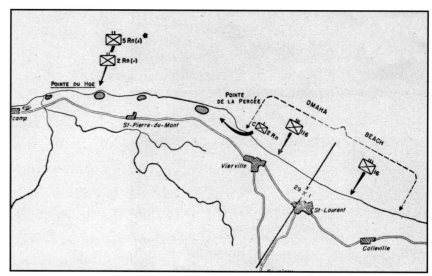

The three other instruments all stand about 235 yards from the shore. The Freya is situated due south of the Coast-watcher, and stands in an octagonal emplacement. The easterly Giant stands unemplaced, but surrounded by a circular trench in the fields 300 yards from the pinpoint on a bearing of 102 degrees true. The westerly Giant, which is also unemplaced, stands 200 yards from the pinpoint on a bearing of 205 degrees true.

The Giants and the Freya are quite isolated, all the operational buildings being grouped closer to the semaphore station and the cliff edge.

RAF vertical taken in February 1944 by which time belts of wire criss-crossed the area.

Company C was probably the first assault unit to reach the high ground here where the cliffs begin. Pointe et Raz de la Percée can be seen in the far distance. The battle for possession of the strong point continued throughout the day. The Historical Division of the US War Department described the difficulty in its monograph on Pointe du Hoc: 'The last effort of D-Day was to assault the anti-aircraft emplacement; the two ill-fated attempts had cost 15 to 20 casualties. Several attempts were made to knock out the anti-aircraft position by naval fire, with the *Satterlee* expending many rounds in futile bombardment. The position was just too far from the edge of the cliff to be blasted off by undercutting fire, and yet was too close to the cliff to be reached directly by the flat trajectory of the destroyer's guns from their lower firing level.'

TARGET XII/41

It is amazing how little remains of the former radar site, all structures having been cleared away.

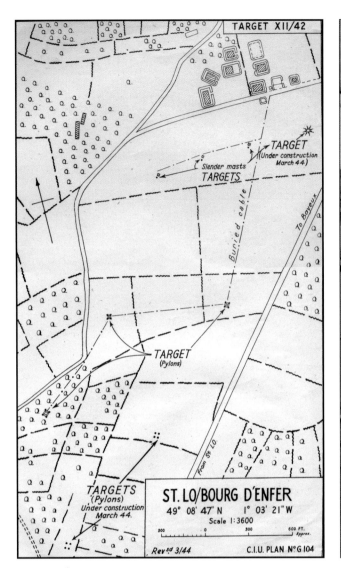

ST LÔ/BOURG D'ENFER

This fighter control station was still under construction when the CIU produced their report, commenting that there was evidence of a fifth transmitter hut and mast due to be added.

DAY FIGHTER CONTROL STATION

Coordinates: 49° 08'47"N 1° 03' 21" W
Grid reference: 526663
Altitude: 380ft

This station is located on high ground 2¾ miles north-east of St Lô, 1¼ miles south of Viliers-Fossard, and immediately west of the highway connecting these two places. The target is dispersed over several fields on the eastern outskirts of the little village called Bourg d'Enfer.

The target is a pylon station under construction (March 1944), and consists of three completed pylons and the foundations for two other pylons. In two fields further north-north-east there are three transmitter huts each with a slender mast beside it, and a fourth hut and mast under construction. There will eventually be a fifth either further eastwards or else at the western end of this line of transmitters.

The receiver pylons are about 60 feet high, the transmitter masts about 80 feet high. Both are placed regularly, the pylons in two lines approximately 250 yards apart, the masts in a single line, each mast being separated from the other by about 100 yards.

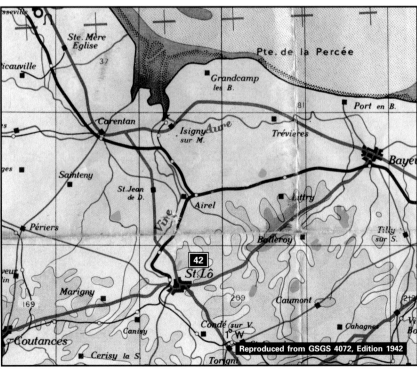

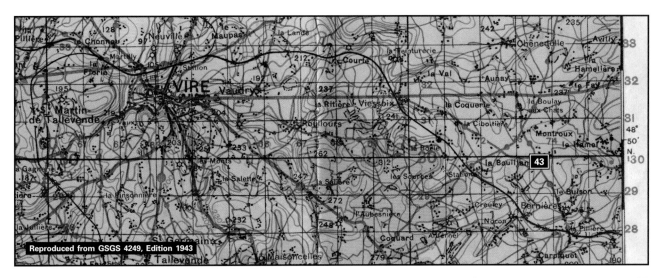

Situated some 40 miles from the coast, Target XII/43 stood on high ground east of Vire. The German code-name was 'Känguruh'.

VIRE/LE PARC

GROUND CONTROL INTERCEPTION STATION

Coordinates: 48° 49'39"N 0° 45' 09" W
Grid reference: 732299
Altitude: 720ft

This site is five miles east of Vire, and one mile south of the main road from Vire to Vassy on both sides of the minor road between Viessoix and Rully.

The target consists of two Giant Würzburgs and a Freya apparatus. The Freya, to which the pin-point refers, is sited south of the road: the two Giants are in the fields north of the road. One Giant is 249 yards away on a bearing of 23 degrees true, and the other is 283 yards away on a bearing of 314 degrees true from the pin-point. Close to each instrument is a semi-sunken building.

The Giants stand on circular concrete bases with a circular trench around them. The Freya is in a circular emplacement nearer other buildings.

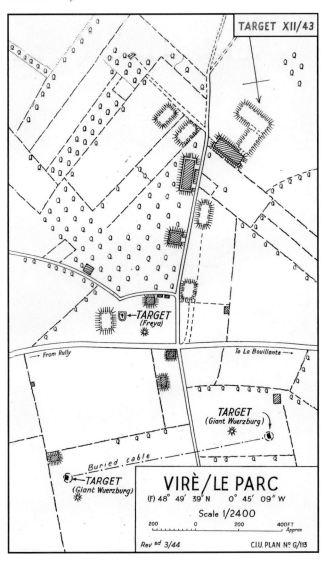

ST VAAST-LA HOUGUE

QUETTEHOU

LE VAST

TARGETS

REVILLE

PERNELLE

Light A.A.

LE VICEL

ANNEVILLE

VALCONVILLE

CANTELOUP

ST GENEVIEVE

MONTFARVILLE

To St Pierre-Eglise

TOCQUEVILLE

VAROUVILLE

BARFLEUR

Light A.A.

CATTEVILLE

GONBERVILLE

NEVILLE

POINTE DE BARFLEUR

AA/164   17.7.43. 1042

NEG.Nº 36275

Seven radar stations were located on the Cherbourg Peninsula. This cover of the one at Le Vicel was taken July 17, 1943.

BARFLEUR/LE VICEL

COASTAL SHIP-WATCHING STATION

Coordinates: 49° 37'30"N 1° 18' 15" W
Grid reference: 370203
Altitude: 345ft

This position was on the eastern side of the Cotentin Peninsula, about 3½ miles south-west of Barfleur and the same distance north-west of St Vaast. The nearest point on the coast is 3½ miles to the east-north-east.

Situated on the east edge of an escarpment two miles to the east of which, at the bottom of a sharp incline, runs the main north to south road between Anneville and Quettehou; in woody, undulating country ¾ of a mile south-south-east of Le Vicel.

The target consists of a Large Coastwatcher with aerial array measuring approximately 30 feet across, and a Giant Würzburg standing on a slightly raised hexagonal concrete base.

The pin-point refers to the Coastwatcher. The Giant is 56 yards south-east of it.

North-west of the instruments are several sunken huts, between which slit trenches run to connect with the instruments. Trenches also guard the approaches by road. The entire site is surrounded by a belt of wire defence.

A typical Large Coastwatcher (known to the Germans as FuMO 5 Boulogne) similar to that at Target XII/44.

141

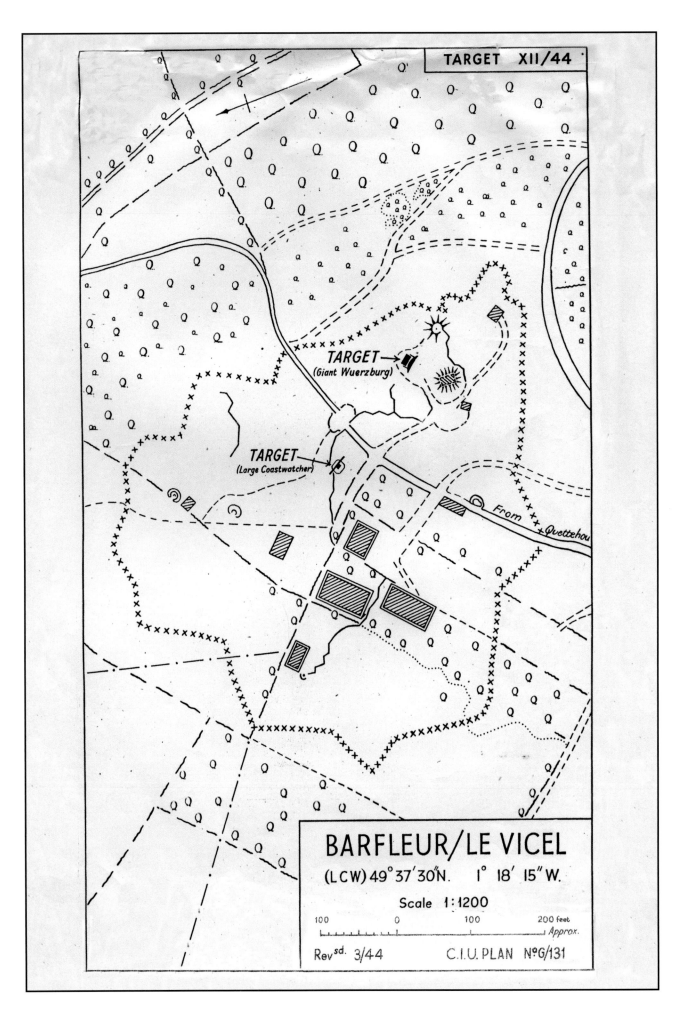

TARGET XII/44

TARGET
(Giant Wuerzburg)

TARGET
(Large Coastwatcher)

From Quettehou

BARFLEUR/LE VICEL

(LCW) 49°37′30″N.   1° 18′ 15″W.

Scale 1:1200

100   0   100   200 feet
                                    Approx.

Rev$^{sd.}$ 3/44   C.I.U. PLAN N°G/131

142

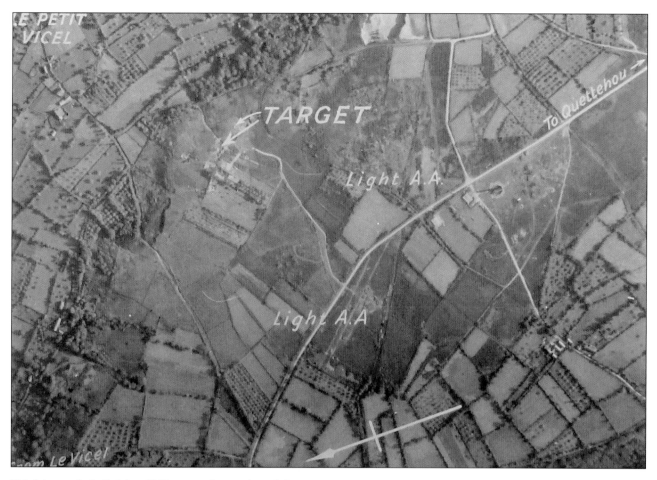

This later sortie in October 1943 gave a clearer view of the target.

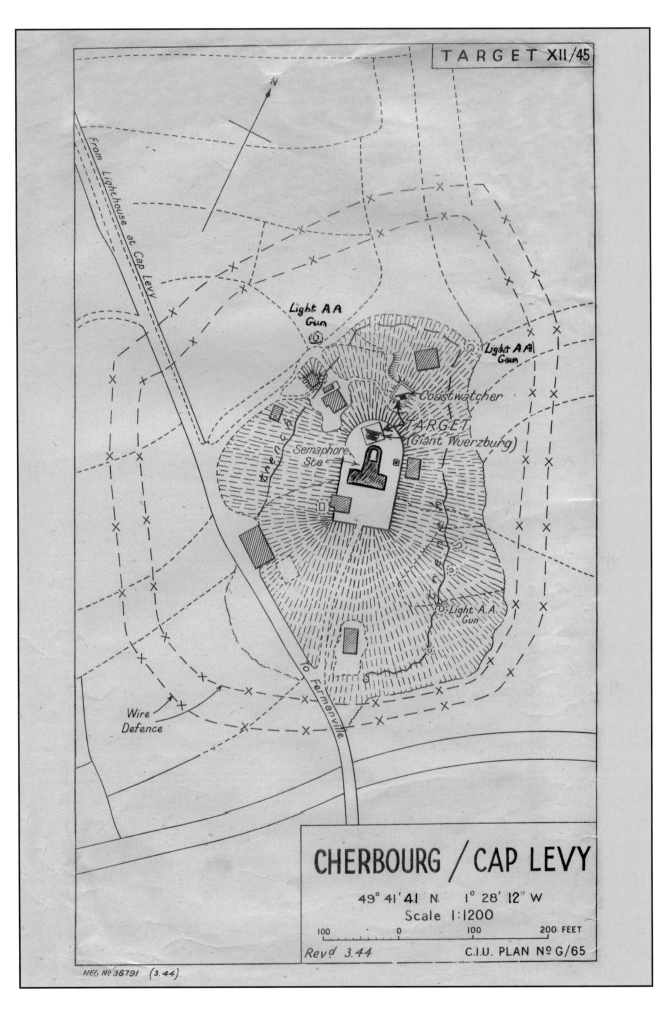

TARGET XII/45

From Lighthouse at Cap Levy

N

Light A.A.
Gun

Light A.A.
Gun

Coastwatcher

TARGET
(Giant Wuerzburg)

Semaphore
Sta.

To Fermanville

Light A.A.
Gun

Wire
Defence

CHERBOURG / CAP LEVY

49° 41' 41" N.   1° 28' 12" W

Scale 1:1200

100   0   100   200 FEET

Revd 3.44   C.I.U. PLAN Nº G/65

NEG Nº 36791 (3.44)

144

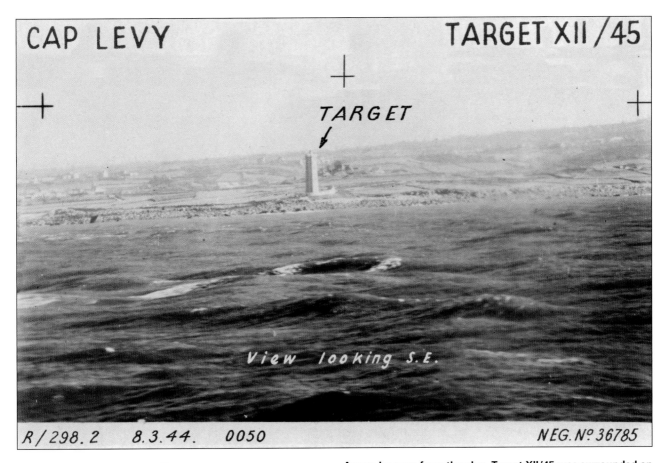

TARGET

View looking S.E.

R/298.2   8.3.44.   0050   NEG. № 36785

CHERBOURG/CAP LEVY

COASTAL SHIP-WATCHING STATION

Coordinates: 49° 41'41"N 1° 28' 12" W
Grid reference: 254287
Altitude: 50ft

As can be seen from the plan, Target XII/45 was surrounded on three sides by trenches and protected by a double belt of barbed wire.

This site was 7¾ miles east-north-east of Cherbourg, situated at the semaphore station on Cap Lévy, about 500 yards inland from the lighthouse.

The target consists of a Giant Würzburg and a Coastwatcher.

The latter stands in a prominent square emplacement just in front of the semaphore station: the Giant is set on a square concrete base in the compound of the semaphore station and only a few yards from the building itself.

CHERBOURG/FERMANVILLE (LA BRASSERIE)

AIRCRAFT REPORTING STATION

Coordinates: 49° 40' 05"N 1° 28' 10" W
Grid reference: 254257
Altitude: 450ft

Below: **This vertical cover of Target XII/46 has been oriented to match the plan. The station was manned by the 12. Flugmelde-Leit-Kompanie of Luft-Nachrichten-Regiment 53.**

Also referred to as Fermanville (La Brasserie), this site lies about seven miles east-north-east of Cherbourg, on the summit of high ground one mile north of Maupertus airfield, and just west of the hamlet of La Brasserie.

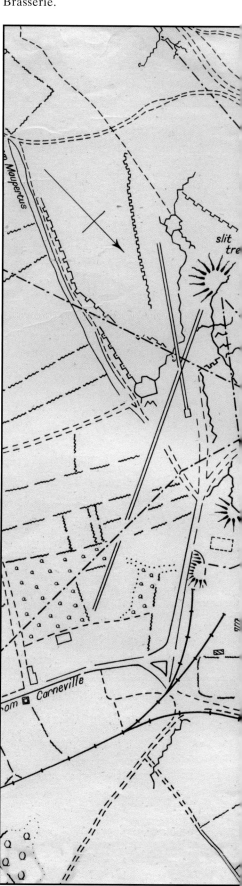

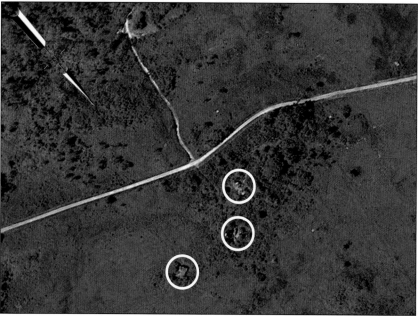

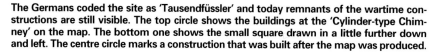

The Germans coded the site as 'Tausendfüssler' and today remnants of the wartime constructions are still visible. The top circle shows the buildings at the 'Cylinder-type Chimney' on the map. The bottom one shows the small square drawn in a little further down and left. The centre circle marks a construction that was built after the map was produced.

The target consists of Chimney radar apparatus of Cylinder type (Wassermann), two Giant Würzburgs and two Freyas.

The pin-point refers to the Chimney, which is sited on the west side of an operational building in the centre of the target area.

The two Giants, both on circular concrete bases, are situated respectively 370 yards north-north-east of the Chimney and 160 yards from the Chimney on a bearing of 58 degrees true.

The Freya is in a rectangular emplacement 400 yards north-east of the Chimney.

Some 260 yards east of the Chimney, in a longer rectangular emplacement, is a Freya with an aerial array measuring approximately 33 feet across.

The whole area is thickly defended by slit trenches, light AA and belts of wire.

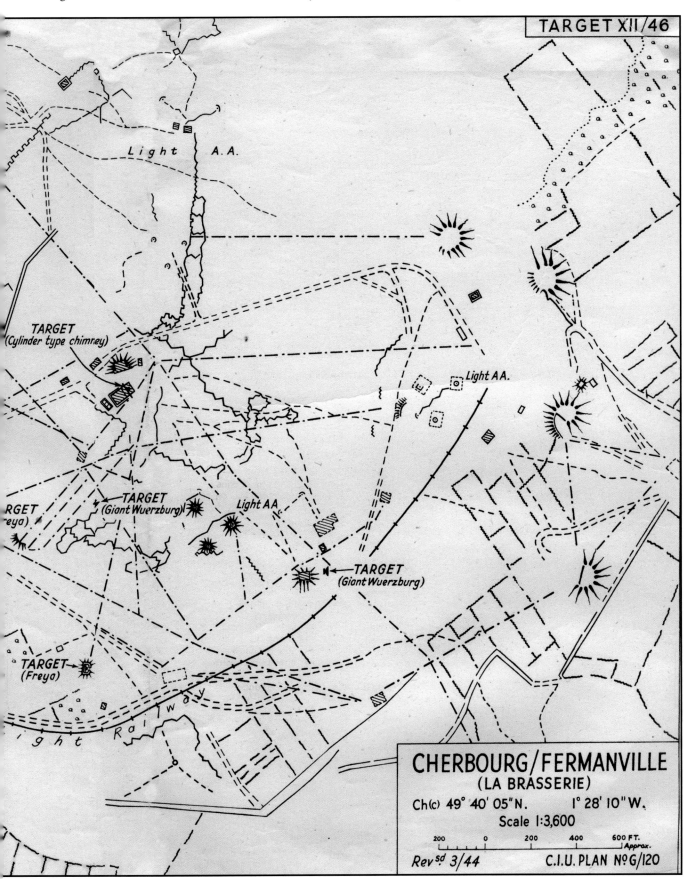

TARGET XII/46

Light A.A.

TARGET
(Cylinder type chimney)

Light AA.

TARGET
(Giant Wuerzburg)

Light AA

TARGET
(Freya)

TARGET
(Giant Wuerzburg)

TARGET→
(Freya)

CHERBOURG/FERMANVILLE
(LA BRASSERIE)
Ch(c) 49° 40′ 05″N.   1° 28′ 10″W.
Scale 1:3,600

200   0   200   400   600 FT.
Approx.

Rev^sd 3/44   C.I.U. PLAN N° G/120

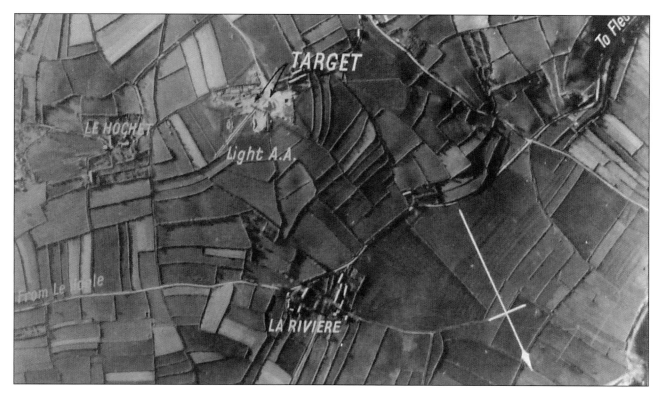

OMONVILLE-LA-ROGUE/ASSELINS

Medmenham designated the Omonville-la-Rogue site as Target XII/47 — see page 141 for the location.

COASTAL SHIP-WATCHING STATION

Coordinates: 49° 42'19"N 1° 51' 28" W
Grid reference: 976312
Altitude: 230ft

This station is located four miles east-south-east of Cap de la Hague, on the edge of high ground about half a mile east of Omonville-la-Rogue, and just under a mile inland and to the south-south-west of the semaphore station on Pointe de Jardeheu.

The target consists of a Large Coast-watcher and a Small Hoarding situated about 30 yards apart in the centre of the area. The frame of the Coastwatcher measures approximately 33 feet in height and 30 feet across. The Hoarding is still under construction (March 1944) and stands on three large concrete blocks which form the base of the instrument.

The area is surrounded by a double belt of wire defence laid out roughly in the shape of a star and is defended by light AA.

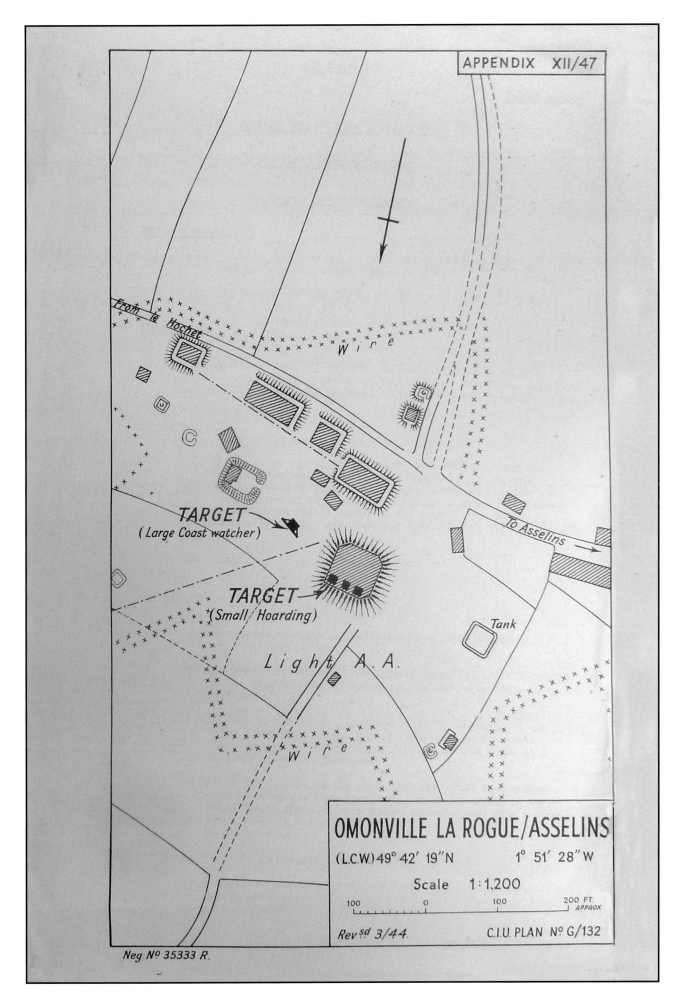

APPENDIX XII/47

From le Hochet

Wire

TARGET
(Large Coast watcher)

TARGET
(Small Hoarding)

To Asselins

Light A.A.

Tank

Wire

OMONVILLE LA ROGUE/ASSELINS

(L.C.W.) 49° 42′ 19″N   1° 51′ 28″W

Scale   1:1,200

100   0   100   200 FT.
                                    APPROX

Revᵈ 3/44.   C.I.U. PLAN Nº G/132

Neg Nº 35333 R.

On July 29, 1940, the destroyer HMS *Delight* was bombed and sunk in the Channel and it was believed that it had been detected by a Freya located in the Cap de la Hague. Five months later Dr Jones and Charles Frank were examining this pair of stereo photographs *(right)* of a site at Auderville on which a tell-tale shadow indicated the presence of a mast or tower. A successive photo showed a shorter shadow, giving the clue that the object was revolving, so Jones asked the Photo-Reconnaissance Unit to take low-level obliques of the site. Unfortunately, the first sortie missed the correct installation, having photographed a nearby anti-aircraft battery instead.

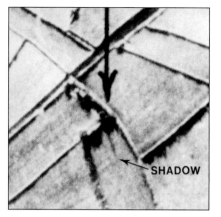 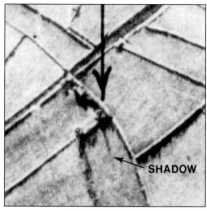

CAP DE LA HAGUE/AUDERVILLE

Below: The mission was flown again on February 22, 1941 by Flying Officer Bill Manifould (who failed to return from a recce flight six weeks later).

AIRCRAFT REPORTING STATION

Coordinates: 49° 42' 52"N 1° 56' 02" W
Grid reference: 922326
Altitude: 165ft

This site is three-quarters of a mile south of Cap de la Hague and about 500 yards from the west shore of the peninsula, and immediately west of the village of Auderville. The target is situated on the north slopes of high ground, to the west of which is a rapid slope down to fields bordering the coast. The road between Auderville and the coast runs directly through the site.

The target consists of two Freyas, one large Freya, and two Giant Würzburgs. The pin-point refers to the Freyas, which are sited centrally in the target area, 30 yards apart, in raised concrete emplacements.

Another 66 yards to the south-south-east, on the south side of the road, is one of the Giant Würzburgs, which is on a circular concrete base. The second Giant is 125 yards west-north-west of the pin-point in a slightly sunken emplacement.

FORMER POWER STATION

The twin Freya radar aerials for the station, which was code-named 'Ammer' and operated by the 6. Flugmelde-Leit-Kompanie of Luft-Nachrichten-Regiment 12, were sited here.

Jones: 'The following day Claude Wavell at Medmenham telephoned to say that he now had the pictures and that they confirmed our suspicions. I went out to his headquarters, returning in time for a meeting that Air Marshal Joubert, AOC of Coastal Command, had convened for that afternoon with one item only on the agenda: to discuss the existence of German radar. The new pilot had the two objects beautifully centred in his picture; there was no doubt that they were radar sets. So at last we knew what one type of German radar looked like; moreover, we had heard its transmission and had heard similar transmissions coming from other stations, whose exact locations it should now be possible to determine on aerial photographs. We could thus find the deployment of the coastal radar chain.'

About 155 yards south of the pin-point, and sited in a rather more isolated position than the other instruments, is the large Freya, standing on a square concrete base with a trench round it. It has a frame aerial array measuring approximately 26 feet across. The area is heavily defended by wire and light AA.

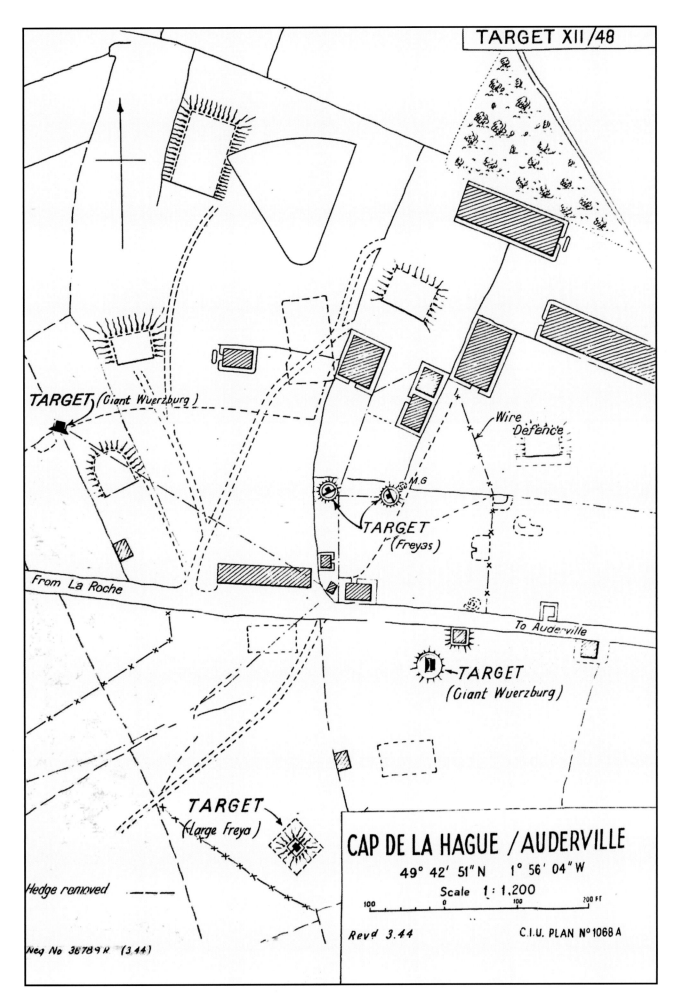

TARGET (Giant Wuerzburg)

Wire Defence

M.G

TARGET (Freyas)

From La Roche

To Auderville

TARGET (Giant Wuerzburg)

TARGET (Large Freya)

Hedge removed ———

Neg No 38789 R (3.44)

CAP DE LA HAGUE / AUDERVILLE

49° 42′ 51″ N   1° 56′ 04″ W

Scale 1 : 1,200

100   0   100   200 FT

Rev? 3.44   C.I.U. PLAN N° 1068 A

151

The two Würzburg Giant radars had not yet been erected when the installation at Auderville was first identified in February 1941.

This Würzburg Giant, [B] in the plan on page 153, was the one described as 'in a slightly sunken emplacement' in the report.

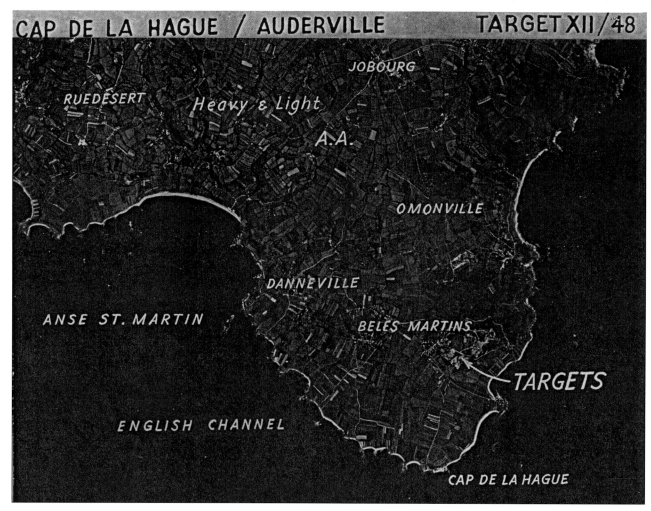

CAP DE LA HAGUE / AUDERVILLE   TARGET XII/48

JOBOURG

RUE DESERT   Heavy & Light

A.A.

OMONVILLE

DANNEVILLE

ANSE ST. MARTIN

BELES MARTINS

TARGETS

ENGLISH CHANNEL

CAP DE LA HAGUE

This was the second Würzburg Giant, [G] on the plan. The two wartime photos were taken by No. 30 Assault Unit in 1944.

The present-day comparisons by Bernard Paich show the two concrete bases as they appear today.

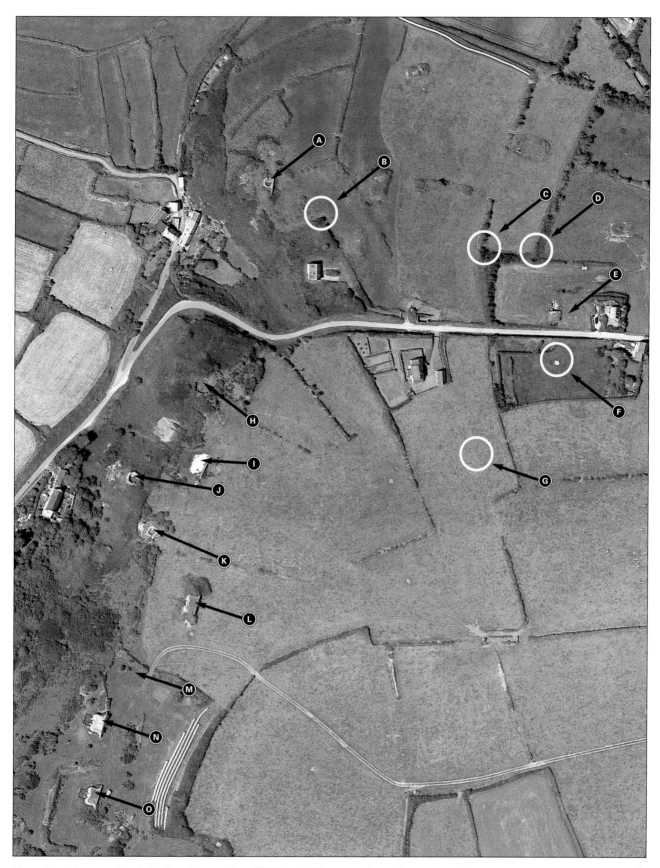

Though nothing remains of the three Freya radars [C], [D] and [G], other constructions at the 'Ammer' radar station can still be seen today including the concrete bases for the two Würzburg Giants. One lies at the corner of the wood [B] and the other just south of the road [F], as well as the electricity station [E], and a 20mm Flak position on top of a shelter [A]. Just south of the station was the powerful coastal battery baptised Stahl. Manned by the 1. Batterie of Heeres-Küsten-Artillerie-Regiment 1262, it was armed with six 155mm guns. Initially, the battery operated the heavy guns from six open emplacements but large R679 casemates started to be built to protect the guns. In 1944, three casemates were completed at Auderville and a fourth was under construction. Several elements of Batterie Stahl can still be seen today: [H] An open platform for a 155mm gun. [L], [M], [N] and [O] are the four R679 casemates, with [M] the one still in an early stage of its construction in 1944. [J] The base for a Seetakt FuMO 2 radar. [I] The power station feeding the FuMO 2. [K] An R636 bunker for the fire control post.

The Cherbourg garrison surrendered on the morning of June 25 when the German commander, Generalleutant Karl-Wilhelm von Schlieben, disobeyed the instruction given him by General-feldmarschall Erwin Rommel, commanding Heeresgruppe B, to 'continue to fight until the last cartridge in accordance with the order from the Führer'. Nevertheless, the 6,000 troops defending the Cap de la Hague were still active. The 60th Regiment of the US 9th Infantry Division and the 4th Cavalry Group sealed off the area but neither strikes by fighter-bombers and mediums nor counter-battery fire by Allied warships could reduce the pocket. The rest of the 9th Division was then brought in to assault and capture the Cape, the operation being planned for June 29. It was a bitter fight but by midnight on June 30 the defenders had finally capitulated.

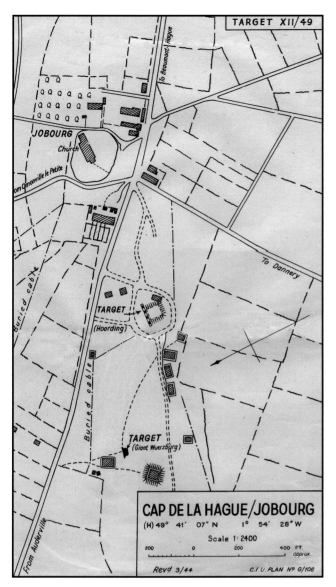

TARGET XII/49

CAP DE LA HAGUE/JOBOURG

(H) 49° 41′ 07″ N   1° 54′ 28″ W

Scale 1: 2400

200   0   200   400 FT.
                                   appr ux.

Revd 3/44   C.I.U. PLAN N° G/106

CAP DE LA HAGUE/JOBOURG

AIRCRAFT REPORTING STATION

Coordinates: 49° 41′ 07″N 1° 54′ 28″ W
Grid reference: 939292
Altitude: 550ft

Situated on the Cap de la Hague peninsula, on the high ground immediately west of the village of Jobourg, and south of the road to Auderville.

The target consists of a Hoarding, to which the pin-point refers, and a Giant Würzburg which is situated 185 yards north-west between two sunken huts. The Giant stands on a low concrete emplacement. Round the base of the Hoarding earth has been mounded up and two huts built beside it.

The attack on Jobourg on May 24 cost the lives of two Typhoon pilots from No. 158 Squadron. During the attack the aircraft came under intense anti-aircraft fire and Flying Officer Harold Freeman in MN410 was hit by Flak and collided with JR527 of Pilot Officer Edward Vallely, both aircraft crashing together within 100 yards of the radar station.

Five kilometres to the south of Auderville lay Target XII/49. The station was manned by the 13. Flug-Melde-Kompanie of Luft-Nachrichten-Regiment 53.

During his research into the attacks against German radio and radar installations on the Pointe de la Hague, French aviation historian Mickaël Simon unearthed this photo of one of the Typhoon's huge Napier Sabre engines.

155

CAP DE CARTERET/ SÉMAPHORE

COASTAL SHIP-WATCHING STATION

Coordinates: 49° 22'28"N 1° 48' 23" W
Grid reference: 993942
Altitude: 220ft

Target XII/50 lies 2½ miles west of Barneville, on the tower of the semaphore station at Cap de Carteret. The semaphore station stands within a small compound on an open field in the cap, surrounded on three sides by ground sloping rapidly down to the shore. Just to the north is the Cap de Carteret lighthouse.

The target is a Coastwatcher set on top of the hexagonal tower of the semaphore station. It consists of a frame with an unusually solid central framework supported by a single slender pillar.

The last radar station located on the Cherbourg Peninsula was at Cap de Carteret on the western coast. *Above:* Before the war, the French authorities had built a semaphore station right alongside the lighthouse and after France fell in 1940 the Germans found it an ideal building on which to mount a Coastwatcher aerial *(left)* — technically a Zerstörer-Säule FuMO 3. By June 1944, the Peninsula had been heavily reinforced, and the Carteret-Barneville area was being held by the 77. Infanterie-Division under Generalmajor Rudolf Stegmann. On June 17 the 47th and 60th Regiments of the US 9th Infantry Division were ordered to cut the coastal road, the German units being methodically destroyed by the guns of the 60th Field Artillery Battalion. Stegmann was killed during an attack by fighter bombers. *Below:* Today a modern semaphore station still keeps watch on the sea lanes between France and the Channel Islands.

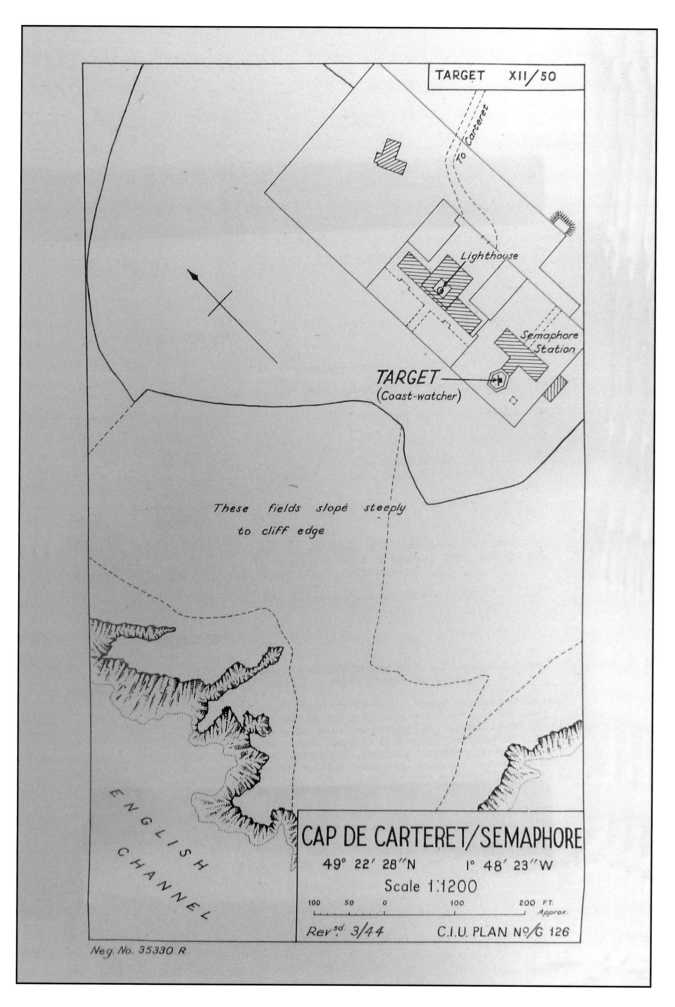

TARGET   XII/50

To Carteret

Lighthouse

Semaphore
Station

TARGET
(Coast-watcher)

These fields slope steeply
to cliff edge

E N G L I S H
C H A N N E L

CAP DE CARTERET/SEMAPHORE

49° 22′ 28″N   1° 48′ 23″W

Scale 1:1200

100   50   0   100   200 FT.
                                Approx.

Rev^sd. 3/44   C.I.U. PLAN N°/G 126

Neg. No. 35330 R

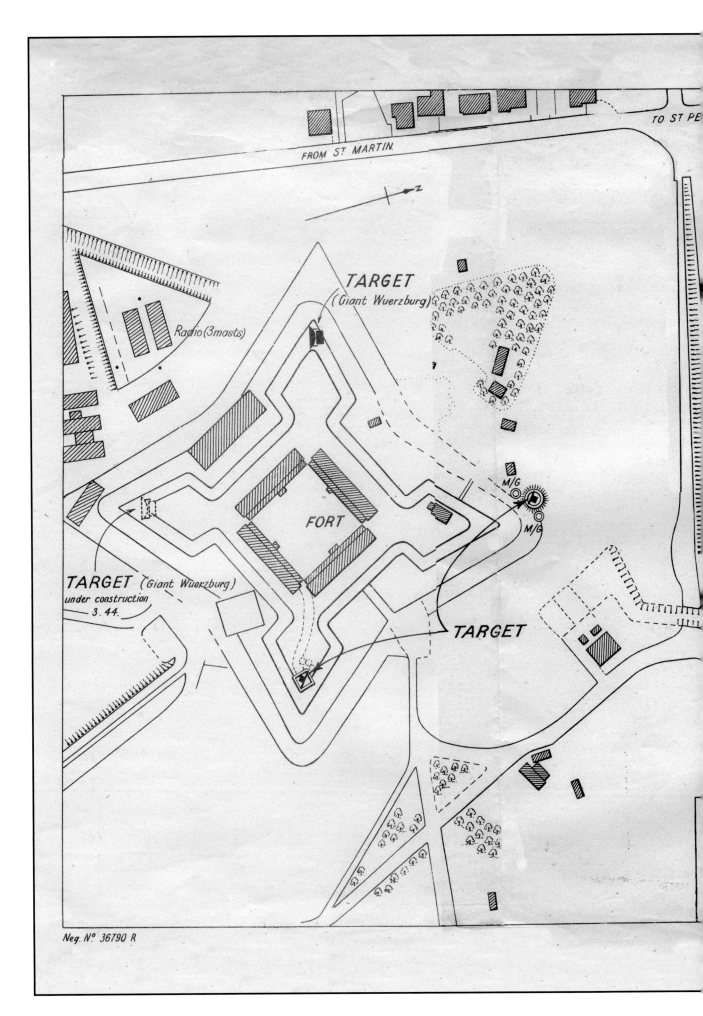

FROM ST. MARTIN.

TO ST PE...

N

TARGET
(Giant Wuerzburg)

Radio (3 masts)

FORT

TARGET (Giant Wuerzburg)
under construction
3.44.

M/G

M/G

TARGET

Neg. Nº 36790 R

158

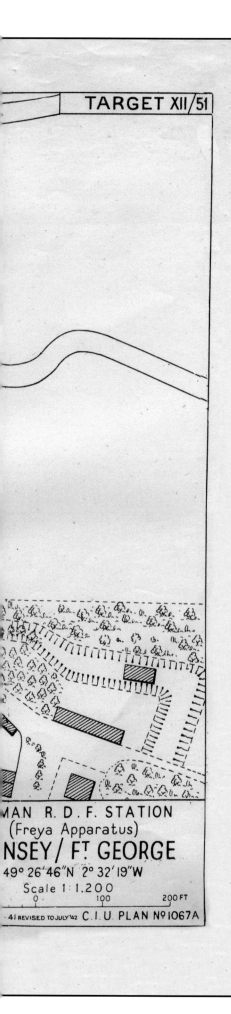

...AN R. D. F. STATION
(Freya Apparatus)
...NSEY / Fͭ GEORGE
49° 26'46"N 2° 32'19"W
Scale 1:1.200
0   100   200 FT
·4·I REVISED TO JULY'42 C.I.U. PLAN Nº 1067A

GUERNSEY/FORT GEORGE

AIRCRAFT REPORTING STATION

Coordinates: 49° 26'46"N 2° 32' 19" W
Grid reference: 130040
Altitude: 300ft

Situated on and around the ramparts of Fort George in the southern suburbs of St Peter Port, and 230 yards inland due east of Soldiers' Bay the target consists of two Freya apparatuses and one, with possibly a second, Giant Würzburg.

The first Freya stands in a circular emplacement on the north-east corner of the fort outside the moat. The Giant Würzburg is installed on the north-west bastion of the fort, and the second Freya is at exactly the opposite side of the fort on the south-east bastion. On the south-west bastion is a base for a Giant Würzburg, which is unoccupied in March 1944. It is possible that a second Giant will be emplaced here.

A thick belt of wire encloses the fort, to the north of which are light AA and machine-gun defences.

Fort George at St Peter Port in Guernsey was first planned as the island's military headquarters during the Anglo-French war of 1778-83 to defend the island against invasion. It was designed in the star shape of redoubts of the period, with Clarence Battery to the seaward side. By the 1830s the fort mounted over 30 cannons. When the Germans occupied the Channel Islands in 1940, they renamed the fort Stützpunkt Georgefest, adding emplacements, two Freyas and two Giant Würzburg installations. Attacks were mounted to try to neutralise the Fort George radar just before D-Day but these are reported as being unsuccessful, Flight Lieutenant John Saville of No. 439 Squadron being shot down over St Peter Port by Flak on June 5.

The States of Guernsey purchased the site (apart from the military cemetery which contains both British and German graves) from the Crown in 1958 and, in spite of its history and strenuous objections from the islanders, ten years later the land was sold to a property developer. The majority of the barrack buildings were demolished for the provision of over 100 private luxury houses.

GUERNSEY/PLEINEMONT

COASTAL SHIP-WATCHING STATION

Coordinates: 49° 26'05"N 2° 40' 24" W
Grid reference: 023026
Altitude: 150ft

As explained earlier, the CIU did not always angle their photos and plans with north at the top, one assumes to help pilots orient themselves for the best line of attack.

Situated on Pleinemont Point on the south-west coast of Guernsey, half a mile north-west of the village of Pleinemont, on a high isolated spot on the headland in front of which the land slopes sharply toward the sea.

The target consists of a Freya apparatus in a square emplacement standing near a long semi-sunken hut.

The target is protected by a double belt of wire defence and by light AA.

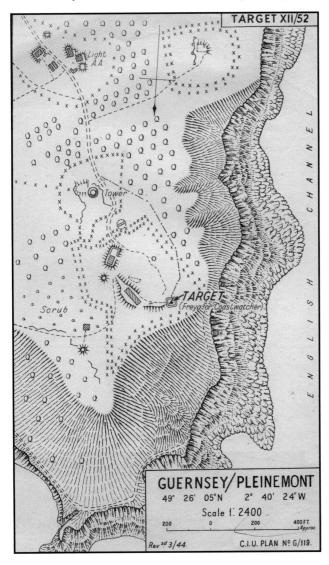

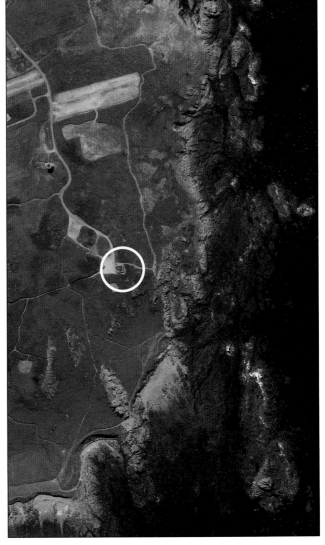

Würzburg radar installations were not only used for early warning; for example, this Giant at La Frie Baton was the rangefinder for Batterie Mirus. This mounted four ex-Russian 305mm guns in open emplacements (circled) giving an all-round field of fire. With a range of 20-25 miles, the battery was a threat to American forces in the Cherbourg Peninsula but, as it posed no threat to the initial landings in France, was not included in the RAF's list of pre-D-Day 'Rhubarb' targets. The mount for the aerial still stands at the old battery command post.

BATTERY COMMAND POST

In 1945, a massive clear-up of ordnance resulted in the loss of many items that today would be classed as unique pieces of the Island's history. Scrap dealer George Dawson soon made a deal for the purchase of all scrap metal on Guernsey for £25,000. Dawson actually sold on much of the material before it was dismantled and the Mirus guns were one of the first casualties. So we are told, he made the first cut personally on June 23, 1947 only to discover that the Russian steel was so hard that a special gas mix had to be formulated before the work could begin in earnest.

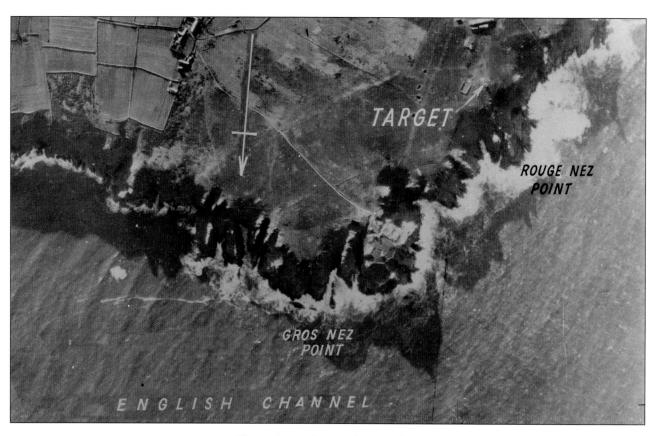

JERSEY/ROUGE NEZ

COASTAL SHIP-WATCHING STATION
Coordinates: 49° 15'18"N 2° 14' 59" W
Grid reference: 719725
Altitude: 225ft

Situated on the north-west tip of Jersey, a few yards from the cliff edge at Rouge Nez Point, north-west of the village of La Ville la Bas, on bare and isolated ground.

The target consists of a single Freya apparatus, in a square emplacement, near which is a single low hut.

Although Jersey was closer to the French coast, this particular station — XII/53 on the CIU's target list — lay at the extreme north-west corner of the island facing Guernsey. One of the huge observation towers, typical of the Channel Islands' defences, still stands a few hundred yards to the south.

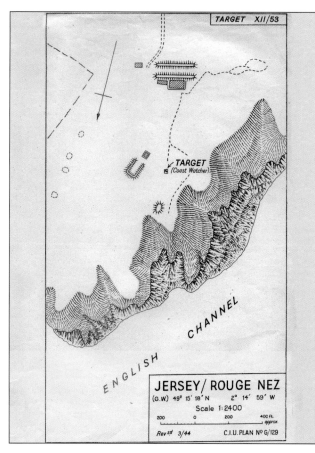

The co-ordinates indicate that the radar station was sited much nearer the cliffs, so we asked Matthew Costard of the Channel Islands Occupation Society to carry out an on-the-spot investigation and he found evidence of the site at the position circled .

ST MALO/POINTE DU GROUIN

These two photos are devoid of German captions but they are good illustrations of the Würzburg installed at Pointe du Grouin. St Malo lies some eight kilometres to the west.

COASTAL SHIP-WATCHING STATION

Coordinates: 48° 42'42"N 1° 50' 36" W
Grid reference: 925209
Altitude: 90ft

In a commanding position on the ridge at the extremity of Pointe du Grouin at the western extremity of the Baie du Mont St Michel. The target is situated just north-east of the sema-phore station and consists of a Coast-watcher and a small Würzburg. The target is rendered conspicuous by the desolate nature of the coast at this point.

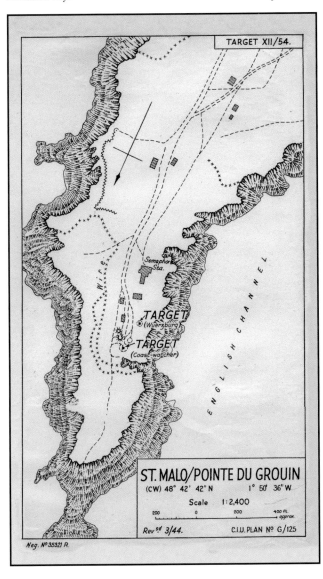

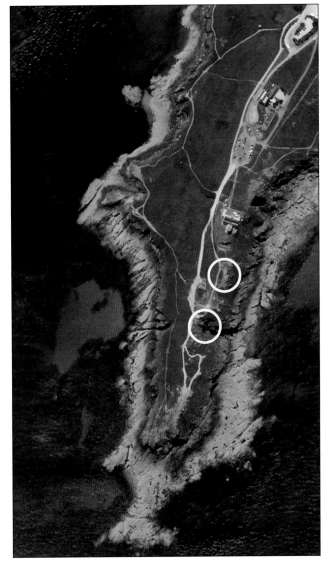

The site at Cap Fréhel was code-named 'Frosch' by the Germans.

CAP FRÉHEL/SÉMAPHORE

AIRCRAFT REPORTING STATION

Coordinates: 48° 40'49"N 2° 19' 02" W
Grid reference: 574195
Altitude: 165ft

The target is situated on Cap Fréhel in the area around the lighthouse on bare isolated ground visible at some distance. It consists of three Freyas, two Giant Würzburgs and a Hoarding.

The pin-point refers to the most northerly Freya which is situated in a square emplacement directly in front of the lighthouse. The second Freya is sited close to the north-west face of the cliffs, 450 yards south-west of the lighthouse.

The third Freya is on the central part of the cape, 450 yards south-south-east of the lighthouse.

The Giants are sited 530 yards south-west of the lighthouse and close to the cliff edge, and 230 yards south-east of the lighthouse on the main plateau formed by the cape.

The Hoarding is approximately 850 yards south of the lighthouse, on a site where excavations have recently taken place.

Complicated trench systems encircle the most southerly Freya and the westerly Giant. Belts of wire defence cover the principal points and surround the lighthouse Freya on the inland side.

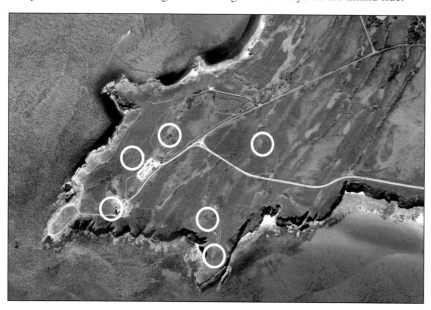

Today, the concrete bases of the two Giant Würzburgs are still visible (the circle in the middle of the row of three on the left, and the one at bottom right) as are some remains of the Hoarding (circled top right).

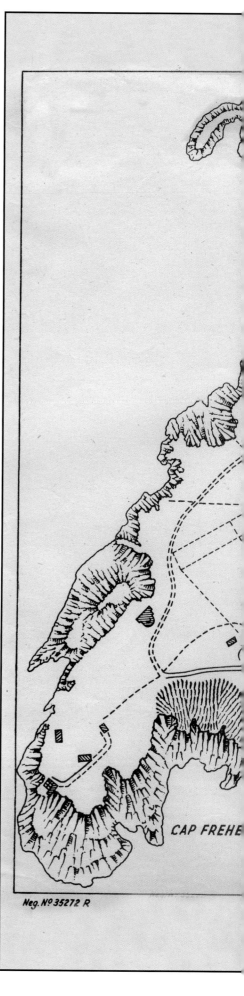

Neg. N° 35272 R

CAP FREHE

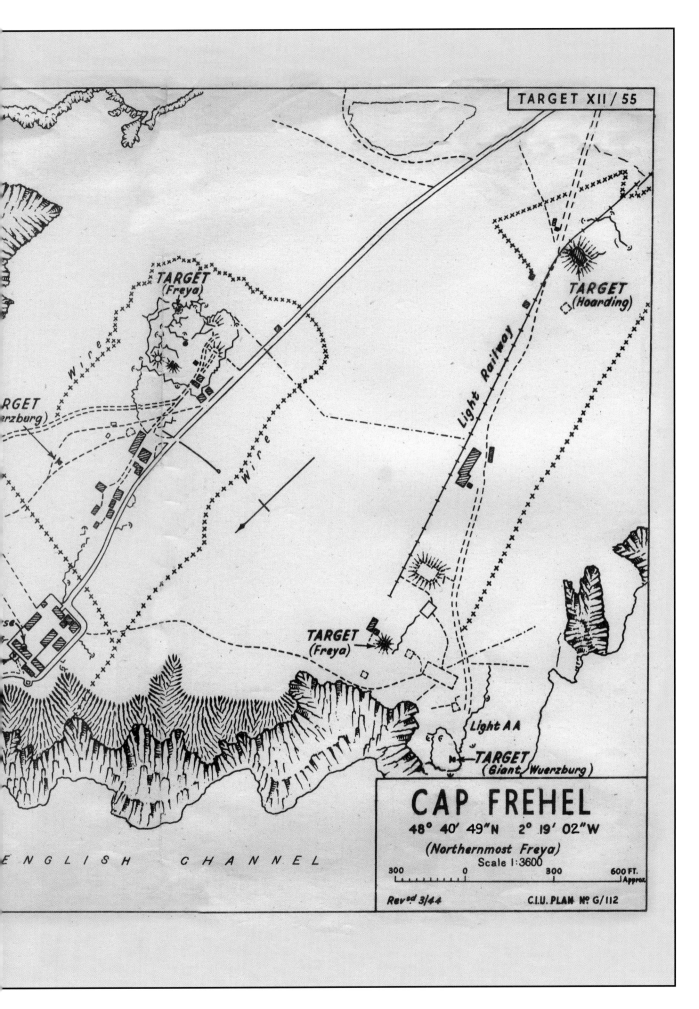

TARGET XII / 55

TARGET
(Freya)

Wire

RGET
erzburg)

Wire

Wire

TARGET
(Hoarding)

Light Railway

se

TARGET
(Freya)

Light A A

TARGET
(Giant Wuerzburg)

E N G L I S H   C H A N N E L

CAP FREHEL
48° 40' 49"N   2° 19' 02"W
(Northernmost Freya)
Scale 1:3600

300   0   300   600 FT.
                                   Approx.

Rev.ed 3/44   C.I.U. PLAN Nº G/112

165

MONTCONTOUR/BEL-AIR

With an altitude of over 1,100 feet, it was inevitable that the Germans would use Montcontour for a radio installation. Today the same site is used for a microwave link.

DAY FIGHTER CONTROL STATION

Coordinates: 48° 19'22"N 2° 35' 05" W
Grid reference: 348812
Altitude: 1,130ft

3¼ miles south-east of Montcontour, on high ground to the north of the narrow-gauge railway between Mont-contour and Collinée, in the western outskirts of the hamlet of Bel Air, at a prominent bend in the railway.

The target consists of five thick lattice pylons about 60 feet high and irregularly disposed in fields south of Bel Air. The pin-point refers to the central pylon, sited due south of Bel Air immediately south-west of the crossroads.

Two fields further west is a line of five transmitter huts protected by blast walls and each with slender mast approximately 80 feet high.

Just west of the transmitter huts is a group of huts, constituting the station headquarters.

Having completed its intelligence files on the radar stations in north-eastern France that were threats to the invasion of Normandy, the list ended with Target 55 at Cap Fréhel. However, six more Ground Control Stations were listed as Targets 56 to 61 (see plan on pages 48-49): Moncontour, Loudéac, Monterfil, Vitré La Haye, Oisseau and Falaise. It is not recorded if they were specifically included at the request of Dr Jones or whether the CIU initiated this at Medmenham. So, although not described as radar stations, for sake of completeness we have included them plus the ship-watching stations at Dieppe/Ste Marguerite, St Valéry-en-Caux/St Léger, Bayeux/Le Mesnil and Calais/Sangatte (Targets 62-65).

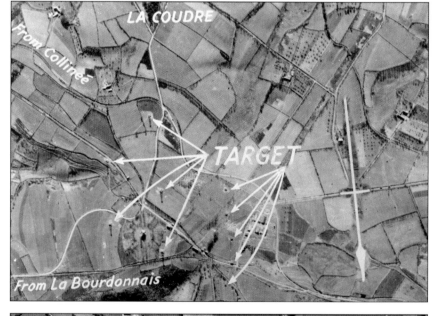

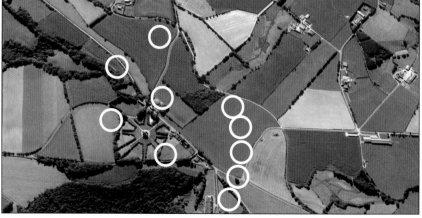

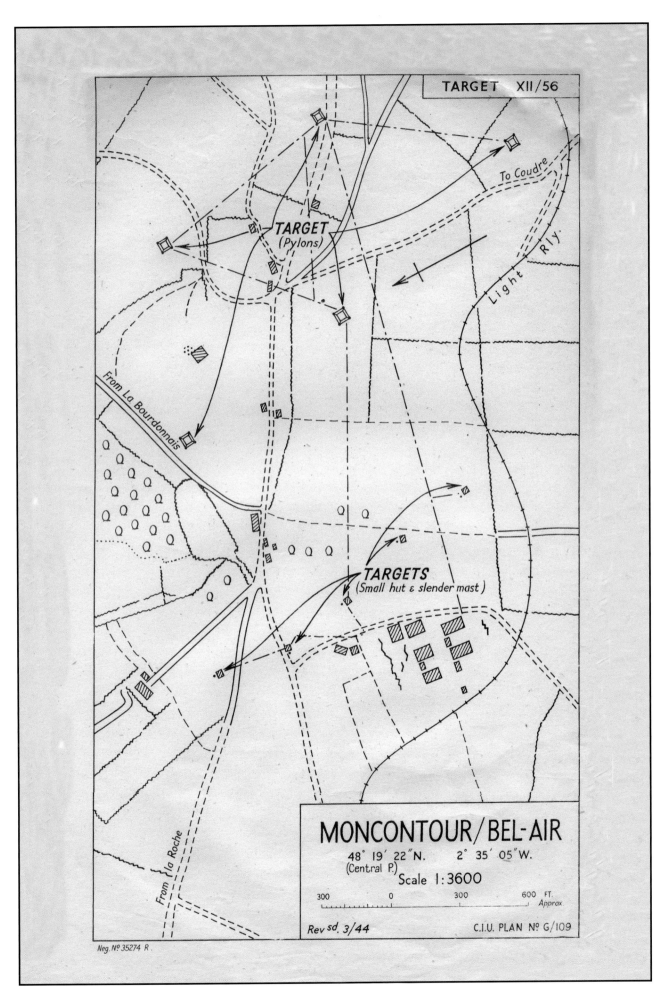

TARGET XII/56

To Coudre

Light Rly.

TARGET
(Pylons)

From La Bourdonnais

TARGETS
(Small hut & slender mast)

From La Roche

MONCONTOUR/BEL-AIR
48° 19′ 22″N.   2° 35′ 05″W.
(Central P.)
Scale 1:3600

300   0   300   600 FT.
                              Approx.

Rev sd. 3/44   C.I.U. PLAN № G/109

Neg. № 35274 R.

167

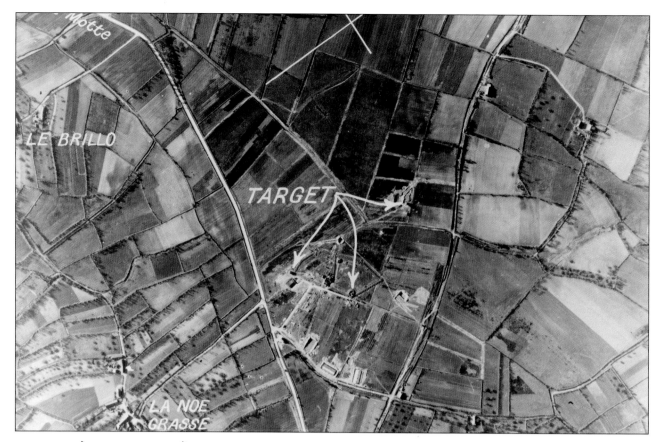

LOUDÉAC/LA RÉCOMPENSE

The transformation between the French countryside as it was made up of small fields is very apparent when compared to the same area today. The German code-name for this site was 'Lachs'.

GROUND CONTROL INTERCEPTION STATION

Coordinates: 48° 14'16"N 2° 41' 40" W
Grid reference: 265722
Altitude: 910ft

Situated on the summit of high ground in open country north and west of the forest of Loudéac, east of the village of La Motte, five miles north-north-east of the town of Loudéac, and 1¼ miles east of the main road connecting Loudéac and Plouguenast. The site is within a large triangle of minor roads running across the plateau.

Target consists of a pair of Giant Würzburgs and two Freya of Pole type. The pin-point refers to the south-westerly Freya which stands in a large hexagonal emplacement and well mounded upon the outside with earth. The Giants stand on open circular bases 276 yards on a bearing of 342 degrees and 173 yards on a bearing of 240 degrees, respectively from the Freya. The second Freya is unemplaced 210 yards on a bearing of 63 degrees from the pin-point.

The operational buildings, which are still (March 1944) under construction, lie to the south of the pin-point and consist of two medium-size huts and the foundations for a third. A fourth hut has been put up alongside the southernmost Giant whilst that for the other is in the foundations stage only.

The site is protected by wire and trenches. Hedges in the immediate vicinity have been cleared.

It was manned by the 7. Flugmelde-Leit-Kompanie of Luft-Nachrichten-Regiment 54.

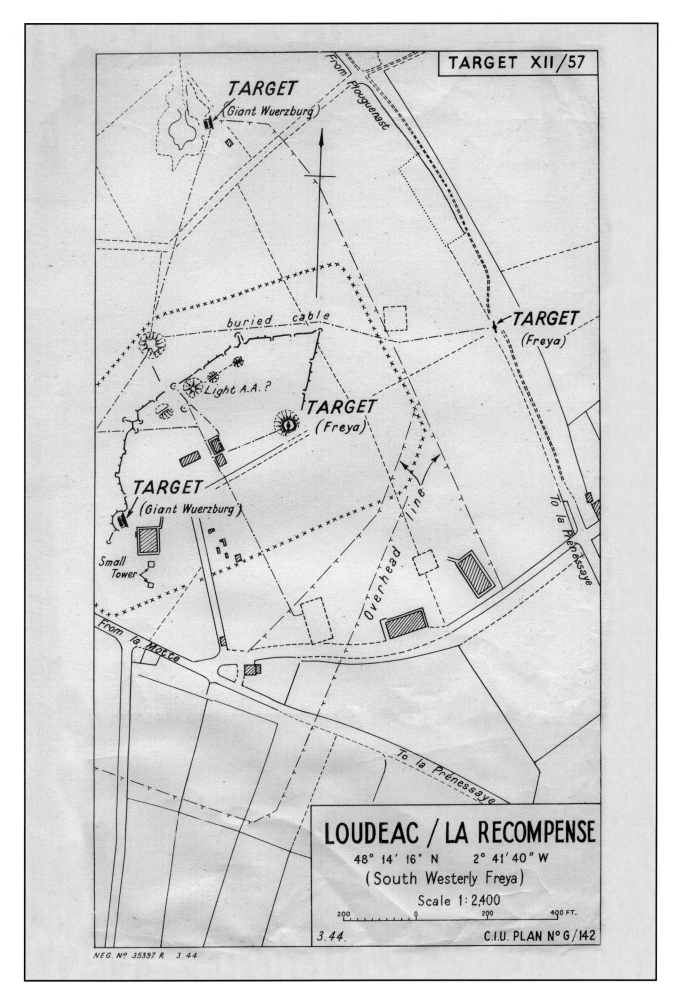

TARGET XII/57

TARGET
(Giant Wuerzburg)

From Plouguenast

buried cable

TARGET
(Freya)

Light A.A.?

TARGET
(Freya)

TARGET
(Giant Wuerzburg)

Overhead line

To la Prénessaye

Small
Tower

From la Motte

To la Prénessaye

LOUDEAC / LA RECOMPENSE
48° 14′ 16″ N   2° 41′ 40″ W
(South Westerly Freya)
Scale 1:2,400
200   0   200   400 FT.

3.44.   C.I.U. PLAN Nº G/142

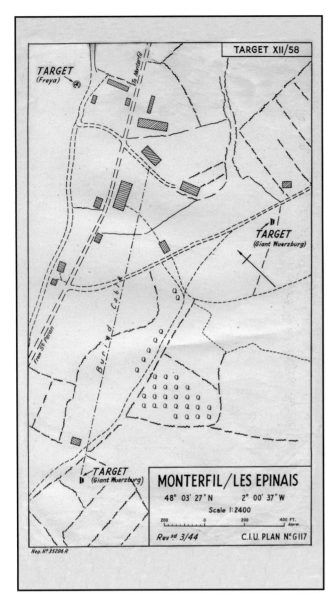

Three of the Ground Control Interception sites — Monterfil, Vitré and Oisseau — were located over 40 miles inland from the coast. Monterfil's code-name was 'Mandrill'.

MONTERFIL/LES ÉPINAIS

GROUND CONTROL INTERCEPTION STATION

Coordinates: 48° 03'27"N 2° 00' 37" W
Grid reference: 761490
Altitude: 320ft

The target lies 1½ miles west-south-west of Monterfil, dispersed on both sides of the road between Monterfil and St Péran, on a crest of high ground, amid fields interspersed with small woodlands.

It consists of two Giant Würzburgs and a Freya apparatus, the pin-point referring to the westerly Giant, which stands in fields south of the road and near a single operational hut.

The second Giant is about 500 yards almost due east of the pin-point and about 270 yards from the road.

The Freya is roughly 380 yards north of the easterly Giant, on the north side of the main road.

The installation was still under construction in March 1944, and as excavations proceed it will undoubtedly become more conspicuous from the air.

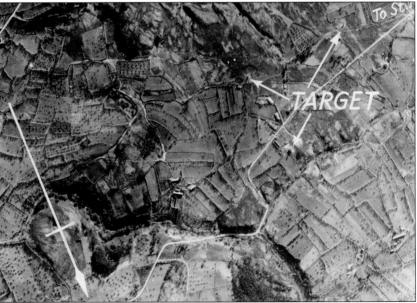

Monterfil/Les Épinais was photographed on February 25, still under construction.

VITRÉ/LA HAYE

GROUND CONTROL INTERCEPTION STATION

Coordinates: 48° 03'01"N 1° 17' 09" W
Grid reference: 299453
Altitude: 300ft

Located six miles south-west of Vitré and two miles east of Louvigné-de-Bais, just over a mile from the main road connecting these two towns, and close to a minor road running northward from Bais and passing west of Torcé and situated in fields just east of the little hamlet of Maimbiers.

The target consists of two Giant Würzburgs and a Freya apparatus. The pin-point refers to the southerly Giant.

The second Giant is sited 428 yards east-north-east of the pin-point. The Freya, in a circular emplacement, is 482 yards east-south-east of the pin-point.

Another inland site, situated midway between Rennes and Laval, it appears that the Central Interpretation Unit had only rather poor photographs taken from two sorties which took place on March 9, with a follow-up ten days later. However, they were still able to produce this detailed plan for the site of Target 59.

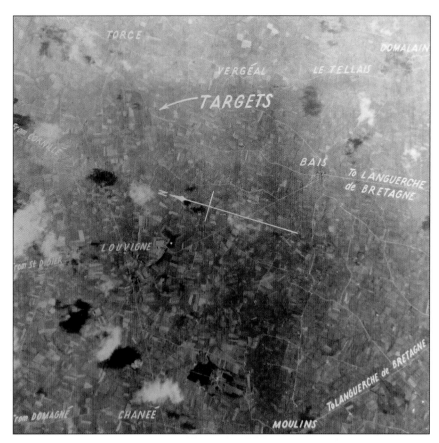

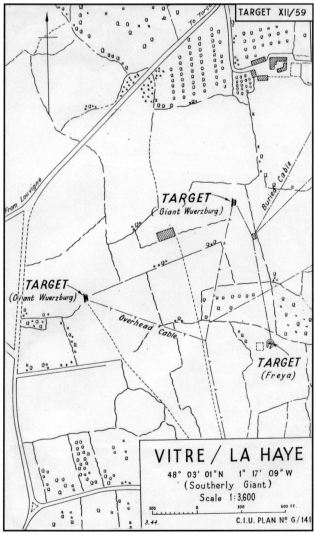

TARGET XII/59

TARGET (Giant Wuerzburg)

TARGET (Giant Wuerzburg)

TARGET (Freya)

VITRE / LA HAYE

48° 03' 01"N 1° 17' 09" W
(Southerly Giant)
Scale 1:3,600

300   300   600 FT.

3.44.   C.I.U. PLAN Nº G/141

OISSEAU/MARÊTRE

GROUND CONTROL INTERCEPTION STATION

Coordinates: 48° 21'39"N 0° 38' 46" W
Grid reference: 778772
Altitude: 440ft

Situated in open fields just north of the road from Oisseau to St Fraimbault, about one mile east of Oisseau.

The target consists of two Giant Würzburgs and a Freya apparatus, the pin-point referring to the more southerly Giant.

The second Giant is situated 360 yards away on a bearing of 329 degrees true. The Freya is 240 yards from the pin-point on a bearing of 23 degrees true. Beside each instrument is a semi-sunken hut. The installation is still under construction (March 1944), and may be expected to become more conspicuous as excavation and building continue.

Situated on high ground, some 100 miles south of Cherbourg, the Ground Control Interception Station at Oisseau maintained watch on aircraft attempting to penetrate inland from Mayenne.

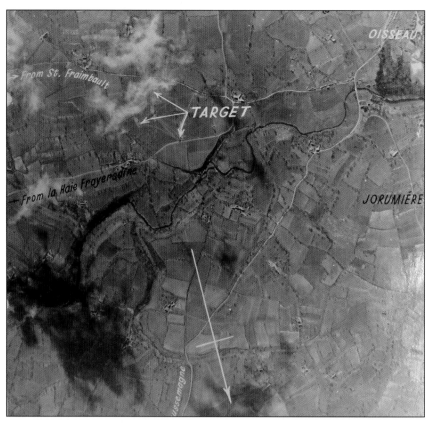

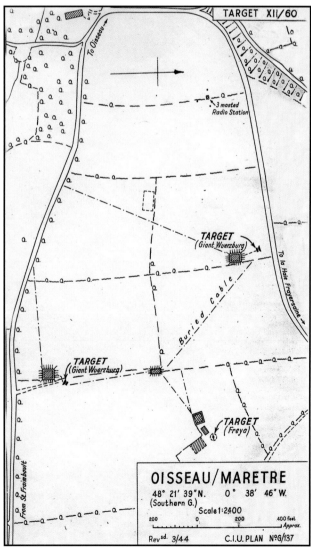

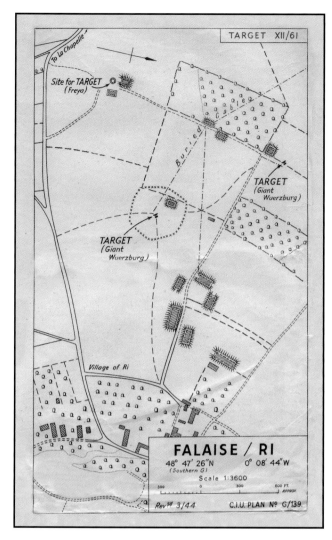

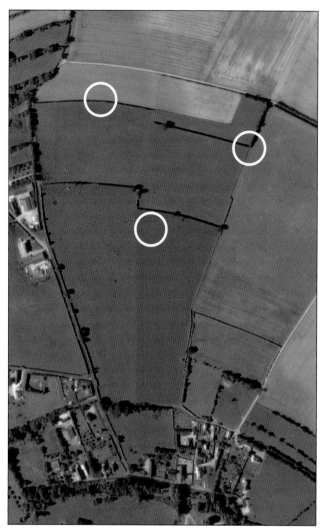

Target XII/61 lay over 35 miles from the coast near the small village of Ri. In summarising the effectivness of the campaign against the radar stations, the RAF narrative explains that 'the attacks were postponed as long as possible so that the enemy should not be able to improvise equipment to cover the gaps in the radar chain which might be created. Attacks did not,

therefore, begin until May 10 when the aircraft reporting stations were bombed. A week later the attacks on night fighter control stations were begun. During the week before D-Day, a series of attacks on 42 radar sites was carried out and in the last three days, six sites chosen by the Navy and six by the Air Force were given special attention.

FALAISE/RI

GROUND CONTROL INTERCEPTION STATION

Coordinates: 48° 47'26"N 0° 08' 44" W
Grid reference: 176241
Altitude: 720ft

The target lies eight miles south-south-east of Falaise, and three-quarters of a mile west of the village of Ri, just north of an isolated and roughly triangular-shaped wood.

It consists of two Giant Würzburgs and a possible Freya, the pin-point referring to the more southerly Giant. The second one stands 306 yards away on a bearing of 324 degrees.

At 300 yards from the pin-point on a bearing of 236 degrees true is an empty emplacement (March 1944) which may shortly be occupied by a Freya apparatus.

Semi-sunken buildings adjoin each instrument, and the southerly Giant is surrounded by a belt of wire defence.

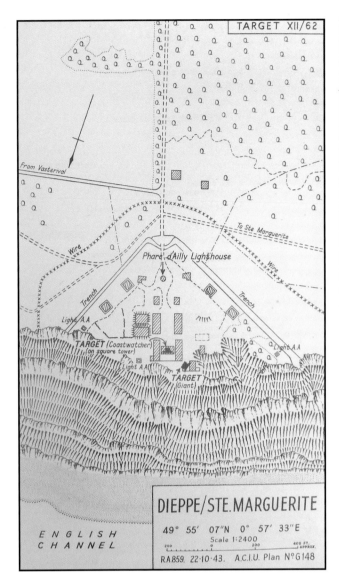

DIEPPE/STE MARGUERITE

Cover of Target XII/62 was available from July 1943, February 14 and April 8, but the quality was poor. A note was added that the site was defended with light anti-aircraft further inland.

COASTAL SHIP-WATCHING STATION

Coordinates: 49° 55'07"N 0° 57' 33" E
Grid reference: 142684
Altitude: 252ft

The target is situated close to the cliff-edge on the Pointe d'Ailly 5½ miles west of Dieppe and three quartes of a mile north-east of the village of Ste Marguerite. The installation is on the seaward side of the lighthouse known as the Phare d'Ailly, which is rendered conspicuous by its triangular-shaped site, a triangle formed by the cliffs on one side and two straight trenches laid out in a V-shape on the inland side. There is a semaphore station 300 yards west of the target.

The target consists of a Giant Würzburg and a Coastwatcher, placed on the lighthouse buildings nearest the cliff-edge. The Coastwatcher stands on top of the square masonry tower situated in front of the lighthouse. The Giant Würzburg is installed on a circular base on the top of a low concrete structure situated just west and to the seaward of the square tower.

ST VALÉRY-EN-CAUX/ST LÉGER

With this station, the Central Interpretation Unit added a comment that the position given in their report was only approximate as they were awaiting further vertical cover.

COASTAL SHIP-WATCHING STATION

Coordinates: 49° 52'20"N 0° 42' 17" E
Grid reference: 956649
Altitude: 230ft

Situated west-north-west of St Valéry-en-Caux, close to the cliff edge 380 yards west of the harbour, and 800 yards east-north-east of the village of St Léger. It is on the seaward side of a small rectangular-shaped wood, which separates on the installation from the houses of the west side of St Valéry.

The target consists of a Giant Würzburg and an apparatus with frame aerial array, possibly a Freya. The Giant stands on a mounded site, with four semi-sunken huts behind and on each side of it, and a large sunken shelter immediately behind it on the inland side. The second apparatus is about 85 yards west of it and slightly further from the cliff edge.

The site is defended by wire on the west and south, where there are in addtion four slit-trench systems with weapon pits. It is possible that there is also light AA defence.

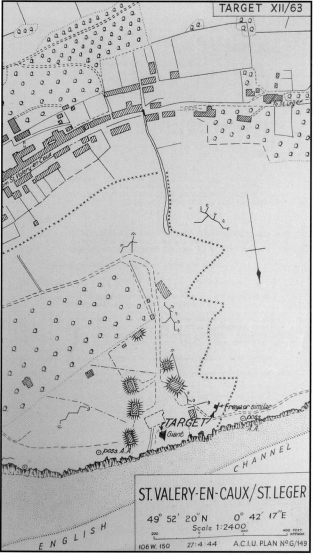

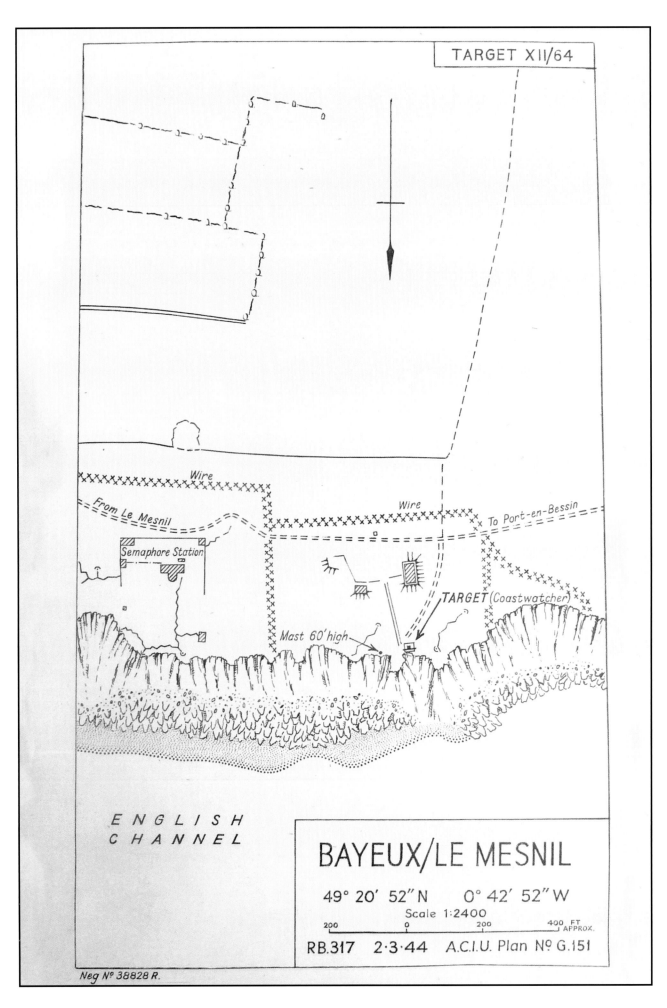

TARGET XII/64

Wire

From Le Mesnil

Wire

To Port-en-Bessin

Semaphore Station

TARGET (Coastwatcher)

Mast 60' high

ENGLISH
CHANNEL

BAYEUX/LE MESNIL

49° 20' 52" N   0° 42' 52" W

Scale 1:2400

200   0   200   400 FT
                                      APPROX.

RB.317   2·3·44   A.C.I.U. Plan Nº G.151

Neg Nº 38828 R.

176

BAYEUX/LE MESNIL   TARGET X11/64

LONGUES

Mast 230ft. high with guys (just off the photograph)

BOUFFRY

TARGET (Coastwatcher)

Semaphore Station

Mast 60' high

ENGLISH CHANNEL (View looking South)

BAYEUX/LE MESNIL

COASTAL SHIP-WATCHING STATION

Coordinates: 49° 20'52"N 0° 42' 52" W
Grid reference: 783876
Altitude: 215ft

Target is located on the cliff edge due north of Bayeux, and approximately equidistant from the little hamlets of Bouffay and Le Mesnil. It is situated in fields about 200 yards west of the semaphore station.

The target consists of a Coastwatcher installed in an emplacement close to the cliff edge. A few yards east of it is a single mast about 60 feet high. There is a further mast on top of the semaphore station whose total height is just under 100 feet, while 400 yards east is another very tall mast 236 feet high stayed by guys.

Behind the Coastwatcher is a large semi-sunken hut and other small constructions.

The area is protected by a single belt of wire defence.

Although Target XII/64 was given the prefix 'Bayeux', that was a somewhat misleading as the site was located four miles away on the coast, just east of Port-en-Bessin. This was a late addition to the CIU target list.

View Looking South

CALAIS/SANGATTE

COASTAL SHIP-WATCHING STATION

Coordinates: 50° 56'11"N 1° 44' 00" E
Grid reference: 786765
Altitude: 148ft

The site is 5½ miles due west of the centre of Calais and stands on the forward slopes of the Noires Mottes foothills facing the sea and immediately in front of the heavy battery emplacements.

Target consists of a single Giant Würzburg in front of which there is a range-finder mounted in an armoured cupola.

A deep and narrow cutting runs up to the underground concrete building below the instrument and a slit trench extends for some 160 yards on either side.

Belts of wire defence enclose the whole area including the heavy guns and a fairly thick concentration of obstacles, probably associated with mines, extends throughout.

Unfortunately, the most interesting site of all is no more, smothered to death by the spoil extracted from building the Channel Tunnel. Target XII/65 — another late addition to the list — was a Würzburg Riese that lay within the perimeter of Batterie Lindemann at Sangatte. This is how the Royal Engineers found it when they were asked to carry out a full survey of the site.

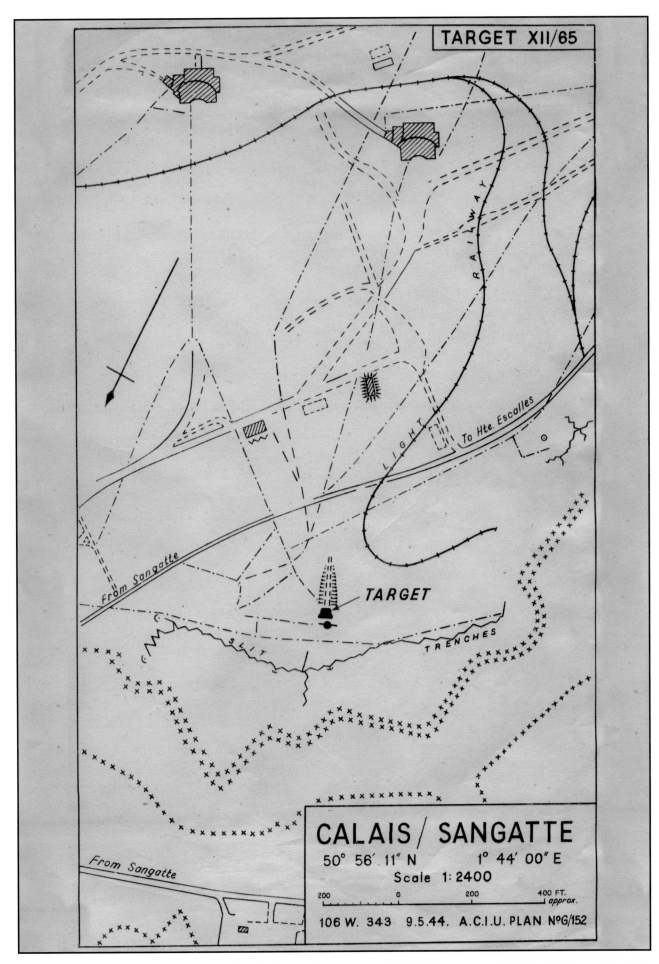

TARGET XII/65

RAILWAY

LIGHT

To Hte. Escalles

From Sangatte

TARGET

SLIT

TRENCHES

From Sangatte

CALAIS / SANGATTE
50° 56′ 11″ N   1° 44′ 00″ E
Scale 1:2400

200   0   200   400 FT.
                                   approx.

106 W. 343   9.5.44. A.C.I.U. PLAN Nº G/152

The plan has north at the bottom as opposed to the battery plan on pages 181-182. Bruno casemate is left with Cäsar on the right.

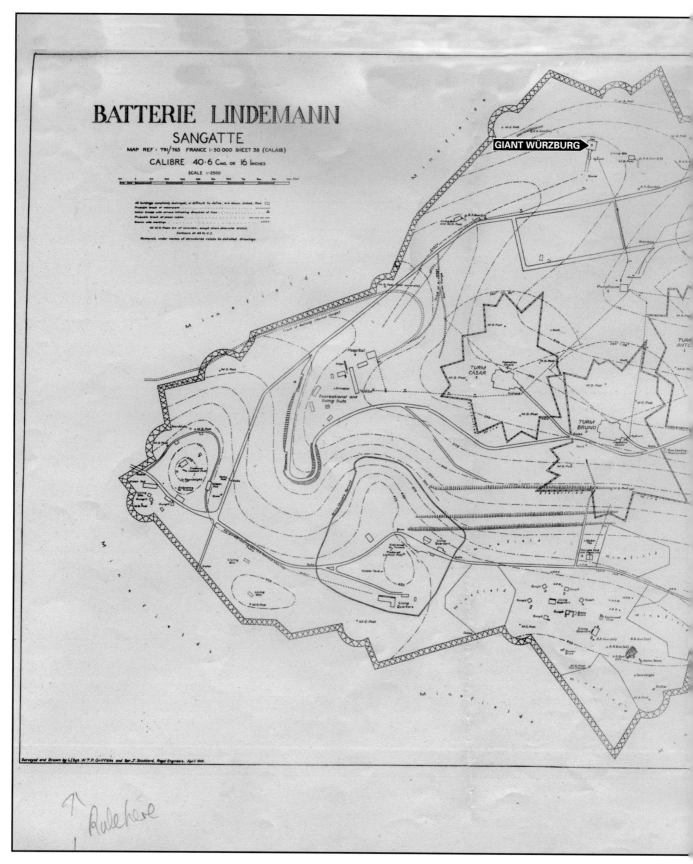

BATTERIE LINDEMANN
SANGATTE
MAP REF : 791/765   FRANCE 1:50 000 SHEET 38 (CALAIS)

CALIBRE 40·6 CMS. OR 16 INCHES

SCALE 1:2500

GIANT WÜRZBURG

The plan to capture the coastal batteries in the Pas-de-Calais was to be carried out by the II Canadian Corps. It began on September 17, 1944 when the Canadian 3rd Division, supported by the 10th Armoured Regiment (Fort Garry Horse), three specialist detachments from the 79th Armoured Division and over 300 guns from 17 artillery regiments, opened the assault on Boulogne. As part of the plan, the 7th Infantry Brigade, which had successfully isolated Cap Gris-Nez at the beginning of the month, was ordered to take the Haute Escalles feature and to silence the guns of Batterie Lindemann at Noires Mottes. The three infantry battalions from the brigade (the Royal Winnipeg Rifles, Regina Rifles and 1st Canadian Scottish) were to be supported by the tanks of the 6th Armoured Regiment and the guns of the 12th Field and 3rd Medium Regiments, but there were doubts whether their weapons could make any impression against the massive casemates of the Lindemann position. Therefore, the corps commander requested that the long-range guns at Dover be

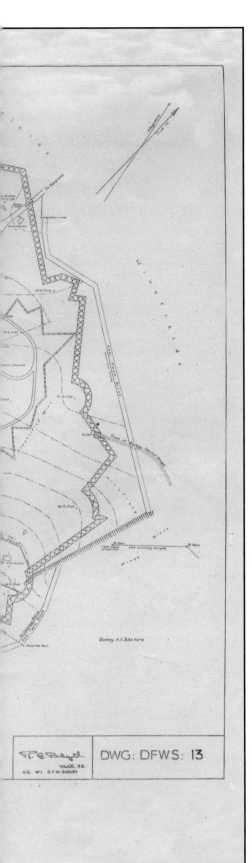

Although the Royal Engineers were charged with clearing the site and blowing up the three casemates, the ruins of Anton, Bruno and Cäsar lying amid the cratered landscape still presented a unique sight . . . that is until 1988 when the valley was used to dump the spoil from the tunnel being dug beneath the English Channel.

integrated to provide extra muscle. The fire-plan for September 17 called for one round to be fired every five minutes from each of the Dover heavies although by the afternoon barrel wear began to take its toll and shells began to fall short. Having failed to dislodge the Germans from Noires Mottes, the Canadian commander now decided to bypass the guns and move instead against Calais, leaving the 7th Reconnaissance Regiment to contain the enemy. At the same time, an air strike was requested to soften up Lindemann and on

September 20 RAF Bomber Command despatched 633 aircraft that dropped 3,372 tons on the battery position. Five days later the 8th Canadian Infantry Brigade began the final assault on Noires Mottes using mine-clearing 'Crabs' from the 1st Lothians and Border Yeomanry to flail a path for the infantry approaching the ridge from the west. Flame-throwing 'Crocodiles' and AVREs supported the attack through the heavily-cratered terrain, and at noon on the 26th the garrison of Batterie Lindemann surrendered.

POSTSCRIPT

We have now covered all the German radar stations along the French coastline that were seen to be a threat to the invasion. (Target plans were produced by the CIU for other sites, identified as being used for day fighter control stations — Targets XII/66-72 — but these were located up to 100 miles inland and so lie outside the scope of this book.) The stations in the Cotentin and Brittany were cleared by the Americans but the majority of the sites in Normandy and up to the Pas-de-Calais fell to Canadian forces as they advanced northwards towards Belgium. There was one particular station that proved a very hard nut to crack as it had been developed as both a radar site and as a strong point: Target XII/39 at Douvres-la-Délivrande. We covered the station and its capture on pages 128-133 but we also asked Bernard Paich to explore for us the area that lies outside the curtilage of the museum. This was where the classic photograph was taken of Sergeant Savage and his Chindits in Hindenburg bunker.

It now lies partly covered over but Bernard was still able to take this perfect comparison. If only we could see if the wording was still there!

Sergeant Savage was commanding a Bofors gun crew of the 102nd Light Anti-Aircraft Regiment which had been formed in December 1941 from the 7th Battalion, The Lincolnshire Regiment. By the time the unit arrived in Normandy on June 17-18, 1944, it had a complement of 50 officers and 900 men. As far as we can ascertain, Sergeant Savage survived the war, the regiment being disbanded on March 4, 1946 when part of the occupation force in Wilhelmshaven. The Hindenburg bunker where he was pictured now lies in fields right outside the land occupied by the museum, there being two other 'named' casemates: Moltke (above) and Scharnhorst (bottom). The capture of the strong point was described in a live broadcast 'from the Normandy battlefront' by Bill Downs, a war correspondent for CBS News although he misnames one blockhouse.

Bill Downs, CBS News, June 18, 1944: 'I have just returned from another one of those "little wars" — an isolated battle which is becoming more and more common in this ever-growing struggle for Europe.

'This little war in no way ranks in importance with the American drive across the Cherbourg Peninsula. Everyone on the British-Canadian sector of the front regards the cutting of the Peninsula the most important single achievement since the Allied troops crossed the beaches of Normandy. But the Battle of the Hindenburg and Bleecker [sic] bastions in which I participated is the perfect example of the type of fighting that is going to occur more and more as our armies advance. I was with the Royal Marine Commandos which took these two strong points. I didn't intend to go with the commandos — it just happened that way.'We haven't been able to tell you before,

but just west of the city of Caen, a group of Germans has been holding out for the past ten days in two very strong defense points. These strong points, about 100 yards apart, were built along the lines of a miniature Maginot Line. They were dug 12 feet into the ground, filled with reinforced concrete with walls three feet thick, and several medium artillery guns. The whole position was set on a rise of ground surrounded by minefields and an intricate trench system. The Germans were so proud of these defenses that they printed the names "Hindenburg" on one of the super pillboxes and "Bleecker" on the other. The Hindenburg and Bleecker bastions were so strong that it was decided to bypass them on D-Day, and let this group of Nazis stew in their own juice. There was no hurry — the Germans couldn't do much damage there. They were completely isolated and could be cleaned out at will.

'Yesterday, the order came to blast them out. The strange thing about this battle was that to get there, you merely turned off a busy Allied supply route jammed with trucks. You drove a block up another road, parked your Jeep up behind the hedge, and on the other side of the hedge was the war. For half an hour, artillery whistled over our heads,

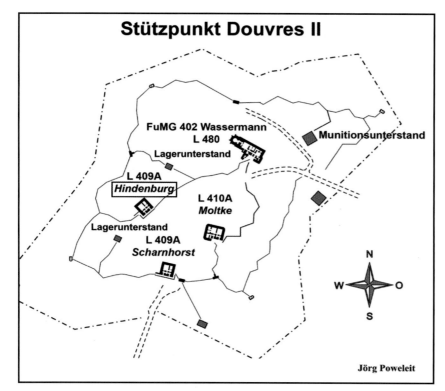

Stützpunkt Douvres II

FuMG 402 Wassermann
L 480
Lagerunterstand

L 409A
Hindenburg

L 410A
Moltke

Munitionsunterstand

Lagerunterstand
L 409A
Scharnhorst

N
W · O
S

Jörg Poweleit

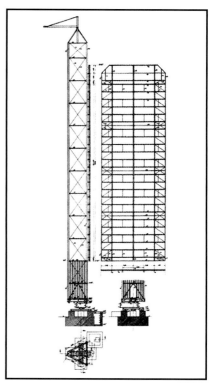

bursting all over the Nazi island of resistance. Direct hits sent bits of masonry high into the air — dust from the bursting shells mixed with the black smoke of exploding mines and a burning gasoline dump to darken the sun. We were only some 200 yards from where the shells were landing, and you had an uncontrollable tendency to duck your head just a little every time a shell came over. The artillery punctuated the barrage with shrapnel shells that burst in the air downward into the trenches.

'Then the barrage stopped and the tanks moved in. There were a dozen of them approaching from two directions. They crawled forward, their machine guns and heavy guns ripping into the super pillbox. Behind them moved the commandos. I was watching the battle with Richard McMillan of the United Press. When the tanks moved in, we couldn't see very much so we decided to walk up behind the nearest one and have a look. Out of the embrasures of the two bastions, heavy German machine guns fired in our direction. We clamped down in the tall wheat, but no matter how low you got you still felt as if you were sticking up as high as the Empire State Building.

'The funny thing about it was that we weren't particularly frightened. We were too excited to be afraid. McMillan, the British conducting officer, and myself were tremendously surprised to find ourselves in with the commandos. We had followed their attacks so closely that we had actually got caught up in the middle of it.

'Up ahead, an assault engineer climbed on top of the Hindenburg bastion and placed a charge of explosives on it. As soon as he lit the fuse he ran like the very devil. We all ducked. The heavy explosion must have blown a hole in the top of the pillbox. Other commandos crept up to this hole and tossed

in hand grenades. One explosion set the whole works off. Out of the hole came a German "potato masher" grenade. It was on fire. We ducked again but it didn't go off. By this time we had reached the trench system. On both sides of us men were going along the trenches with their Tommy guns. A tank assaulted one of the trenches and behind it was a young radio operator

calmly chewing a stalk of wheat, waiting to flash the words that the bastion had been taken. Shouts of "come on out of there you Nazi so-and-sos" and "keep your hands up you such-and-such" announced the arrival of the 1st Troop. Then they began to pop up like prairie dogs. All told, there were between 150 and 200 of them. For the number of them, the Nazis resisted surprisingly

The surviving bunkers for the strong point now lay outside the curtilage of the museum.

Sergeant Savage's crew have taken over one of the enemy gun-pits for their Bofors.

weakly. It took only two squadrons of commandos to dig them out. The tanks merely stood by and watched after they had escorted these troops into position. We lined them up; they were as shaken a group of men as I've ever seen.

'There were all shapes and sizes of Nazis. Big ones, little ones, old, and young. But the most surprising discovery made was a large number of ordinary chicken's eggs in the bastion. The surprise was that these eggs were fresh. There also

was plenty of food, and we shared a bottle of brandy with the victorious commandos. It was a glorious feeling being in on a success like that. But even so, I believe it's the last time that I want to be that close to a practicing commando in action.'

On June 16, Canadian war photographer Lieutenant Ken Bell pictured the remains of Target No. 39 at Douvres-la-Délivrande.

One of the two Giant Würzburg's of Target 41 at Pointe et Raz de la Percée (see pages 135-137).

Index

COMPILED BY PETER B. GUNN

Note: Page numbers in *italics* refer to captions. There may also be textual references on these pages.

Abbeville *see* Vaudricourt
Aberdeen University *30, 46*
Aerofilms Ltd *6*
Air Ministry
   Directorate of Intelligence 24
   Historical Branch 23
   Photographic Interpretation
      Unit *6*
Aircraft
   Typhoon *126*
      JR527 *155*
      MN410 *155*
      MN454 *27*
Aircraft Operating Company (AOC) *6*
Airfields
   Benson 25
   Dishforth 27
   Heston *29*
   Mardick, Gravelines 56
   Maupertus 146
   Northolt *127*
   Oakington *6*
   Pardubice, Czech Rep. *23*
   Ringway 27

Airfields — continued
   St Eval *29*
   Thorney Island *109, 127*
   Thruxton 28
Allerton, Sean *7*
Amiens *see* Montrelet
Andover *27, 28*
Anneville 141
Arras *90*
Arromanches (Target No. 40) *17, 21, 22, 48, 134*
Asselins *see* Omonville-la-Rogue
Atlantic Wall *10, 60, 115, 132*
Au Fèvre wireless transmitting station 21
Aubigny *see* Frévillers
Audembert 70
Auderville, Cap de la Hague (Target No. 48) *17, 22, 48, 150–154, 155*
Audresselles 70
Ault 99

Barfleur *see* Le Vicel
Barneville *156*
Barr, Robert (BBC) *132*
'Basket' (Würzburg Riese) radar (Douvres-la-Délivrande) *128*
Basly *128*
Bayeux *see* Le Mesnil
Bayonne 46
Bazancourt 118
BBC broadcasts *132, 133*
Bel-Air *see* Montcontour

Bell, Lt Ken *186*
Bellevue, Cap Gris-Nez (Target No. 9) 17, *48, 64, 70–71*, 72
'Benito' radar *9*, 15
Berck-sur-Mer (Target No. 22) 17, *48, 92–93*
Bergueneuse 88
Bernaville 96
Bernay *see* La Chalière
Beveren, Arthur van *115*
Bletchley Park *46*
Bodo, Norway 24
Bois de l'Enclos 76
Books
   A Drop Too Many (Frost) *43*
   Green Beach (Leasor) *47*
   Most Secret War (Jones) *29, 30*
Bordeaux 24
Bouffay 177
Boulogne *110, 180*
   'Fortress' ('Festung') status *79*
   Göring's HQ *10*
   Mont Couple wireless station 21
   see also Boursin; Cap d'Alprech; Hardelot; Mont Lambert; Monument
Boulogne radar *see* 'Coastwatcher' radar, Large
Bourg d'Enfer, Saint-Lô (Target No. 42) 17, *48, 138*
Boursin, Boulogne (Target No. 12) 17, *48, 64, 76–77*
Bresle, River *100*

Brittany
  radar sites 15, *110, 168–169, 182*
  see also St Malo
Brooker, W/Cdr Richard 20
Bruneval *110, 112*
  Raid (1942) 13, *24–46*, 47, *103, 114*
    château (code-name 'Lone
    House') 28, *31*, 35
      German Report 35–36
      Hill 102 35, 36
      Interim Report *38–41*
      Presbytère Farm (code-name
      'Rectangle') 28, 35
      Stella Maris villa 33

Caen *131*, 134, 183
  see also Douvres-la-Délivrande
Calais *see* Pas-de-Calais; Sangatte
Calais B radar *see* 'Coastwatcher'
  radar
Canal des Dunes, Gravelines *56*
Canaples 96
Cap Blanc-Nez *110*
  radar station (German code-name
    Düsseldorf - Target No. 5) 17,
    22, *48*, *60–64*
  see also St Pol
Cap d'Alprech, Boulogne
  Target No. 15A (German code-name
    Pantoffelblume) 17, *48*, *64*, *80–81*
  Target No. 15B 17, *48*, *64*, *82*
Cap d'Antifer radar stations 21, 22,
  35, *36, 127*
  Sémaphore (Target No. 31) 17,
    48, *110–111*, *115*
  Target No. 32 (German code-name
    Auerhahn) 17, *48*, *112–115*
Cap de Carteret, Sémaphore
  (Target No. 50) *156–157*
Cap de la Hague *see* Auderville;
  Jobourg; Omonville-la-Rogue
Cap de la Hève (Target No. 35) *15*,
  17, *48*, *120–121*
Cap Fréhel 15, *48*, *110, 182*
  Sémaphore (German code-
    name Frosch - Target No. 55)
    17, *48*, *164–165*, *166*
Cap Gris-Nez *10, 180*
  radar station (German code-name
    Bumerang - Target No. 7) 17,
    48, *64*, *66–67*
  see also Bellevue; Onglevert; Pointe
    du Riden; Wattermel St George
Cap Lévy, Cherbourg (Target No. 45)
  17, *48*, *144–145*
Caude-Côte, Dieppe (German code-
  name Dickhäuter - Target No. 27)
  13–14, 16, 17, 23, *48*, *101–103*
Caudebec-en-Caux 117
Cayeux *110*
  see also Nouveau Brighton
Cemeteries
  Dijon, Les Péjoces Communal
    Cemetery *45*
  Fort George, St Peter Port,
    Guernsey *159*
  Leffrinckoucke Communal
    Cemetery *55*
Central Interpretation Unit (CIU)
  see Medmenham
Channel Islands *see* Guernsey;
  Jersey

Channel Islands Occupation
  Society *162*
Chapelle de la Vierge, Fécamp
  (Target No. 30) 17, *48*, *108–109*
Charteris, Lt Euan, MC (commands
  'Nelson') 28, 33
Chaveau, Charles (code-name
  'Charlemagne') 27
Cherbourg Peninsula (Cotentin)
  German surrender *154, 182*
  see also Auderville; Cap de
    Carteret; Cap Lévy; Fermanville;
    Jobourg; Le Vicel
'Chimney' radar 8, 15, 47, *110*
  Box 9, 17, *112*
  Cylinder 9, 11, 17, 78, 99, *114, 128,
    146*, 147
  Girder 9, *112*
  see also Wassermann radar
Chindits and Hindenburg bunker *182*
'Coastwatcher' radar 8, *18–19*
  at Arromanches 21, *134*
  at Berck-sur-Mer 93
  at Cap d'Alprech 80, 82
  at Cap d'Antifer *110, 112*
  at Cap de Carteret *156*
  at Cap de la Hève 121
  at Cap Lévy 145
  at Chapelle de la Vierge *108*
  at Fort des Dunes, Dunkirk *52–55*
  at Hardelot 83
  at Houlgate, Sémaphore *126*
  at Le Mesnil, Bayeux 177
  at Le Vicel *141*
  at Mont Huon 100
  at Mont Lambert 79
  at Omonville-la-Rogue 148
  at Petit-Fort-Philippe *58*, 59
  at Pleinemont, Guernsey 160
  at Pointe du Riden 68
  at Pointe et Raz de la Percée *135*, 136
  at Rouge Nez, Jersey *162*
  at St Malo, Pointe du Grouin *163*
  at Ste Marguerite, Dieppe *174*
  at St Pol 65
  at St Valéry-en-Caux, St Léger *175*
  at Sangatte *178*
  'Large Coastwatcher' 8, 15
Cockfosters, Trent Park 37
Code-names, German
  Auerhahn 112
  Baumläufer 124
  Biene *118*
  Bulldogge 87
  Bumerang 67
  Dahlie 52
  Dickhäuter 101
  Distelfink 128
  Dora 106
  Düsseldorf 60
  Eber 75
  Fliege 105
  Frosch 164
  Frundsberg 67
  Gertrud 121
  Ibis 76
  Imme 135
  Känguruh 139
  Krimhild 58
  Krokus 78
  Lachs 168
  Mandrill 170

Code-names, German — continued
  Pantoffelblume 80
  Peilstand 3, 65
  Skorpion 99
  Tausendfüssler 146
Collé, Jacques *103*
Collinée 166
Costard, Matthew *162*
Cotentin Peninsula *see* Cherbourg
Cox, F/Sgt Charles ('Private Newman'),
  MM 13, 28, *29*, *37*, *46*, 47, *103*
Cran-aux-Oeufs 68, 69

D-Day *see* Operation 'Overlord'
Darmstadt 23
Dawson, George *161*
De Gaulle, Gén. Charles *42, 43*
Deauville 126
Decroos, Daniel *55*
Dieppe *100*, 118
  raid (1942) 13, 47, *101, 103*
  see also Caude-Côte; Ste Marguerite
Douvres-la-Délivrande
  'Distelfink' strong point *128, 182*
  Hindenburg bunker *182–184*
  Moltke bunker *183*
  radar museum 23, *132, 182–184*
  radar station (Target No. 39) 16,
    17, 20, *48*, *128–133, 182*
  Scharnhorst bunker *183*
Dover, long-range artillery *180–181*
Dover Patrol (World War One RN
  patrol) 60, 65
Downs, Bill (CBS News) *183–185, 183*
Duff Cooper, Alfred (later 1st
  Viscount Norwich), British
  Ambassador to France 42
Duff Cooper, Lady Diana 42
Dunkirk *53, 55*
  see also Fort des Dunes

Enigma (Bletchley Park) 46
Épinay-sur-Duclair, Yvetot (Target
  No. 33) 17, *48*, *116–117*
Étaples 88
Étretat 110
  Villa Orphée *33*
Évreux 122

Falaise, Ri (Target No. 61) 17, *48*,
  166, 173
Farnborough, Royal Aircraft
  Establishment (RAE) 23, *37*
Fécamp, Chapelle de la Vierge
  (Target No. 30) 17, *48*, *108–109*
Fehmarn 23
Felzerhaken naval radar station 23
Fermanville (La Brasserie),
  Cherbourg (German code-name
    Tausendfüssler - Target No. 46)
    17, *48*, *146–147*
Ferme d'Urville wireless station 21
Films, *Metropolis* 55
Forêt d'Hardelot 84
Forges 118
Formerie 118
Fort de l'Est *see* Fort des Dunes
Fort des Dunes, Dunkirk (Target
  No. 2) 17, *48*, *52–55, 59*
Fort George, Guernsey *see* Guernsey
Framezelle, 'Grosser Kurfürst'
  battery *67*

Franco-Prussian War *53*
Frank, Dr Charles 24, *150*
Freeman, F/O Harold 127, *155*
Frévillers, Aubigny (Target No. 21) 17, *48*, *90–91*
Freya radar *8*, 10, *11*, 12, 17, *23*, 24
  at Auderville *150*
  at Bellevue, Cap Gris-Nez *70*
  at Bruneval 25, 27, 35, 36, 38
  at Cap Blanc-Nez 60
  at Cap d'Alprech 80, *82*
  at Cap d'Antifer *112*
  at Cap de la Hève *15*
  at Cap Fréhel 164
  at Caude-Côte 101, *103*
  at Douvres-la-Délivrande *128*, *132*
  at Épinay-sur-Duclair *117*
  at Falaise, Ri 173
  at Fermanville 147
  at Fort George, Guernsey *159*
  at Le Clipon 56
  at Le Parc 139
  at Le Theil-Nolent *122*
  at Les Épinais, Monterfil 170
  at Loudéac 168
  at Manneville-ès-Plains 104, 105
  at Mont Violette 84
  at Montrelet 96
  at Oisseau, Marêtre 172
  at Onglevert 75
  at Plage Ste Cécile 86
  at Pleinemont, Guernsey 160
  at Pointe et Raz de la Percée *14*, 21, 135, 136
  at Prédefin *88*, 89
  at Rouge Nez, Jersey 162
  at St Léger 175
  at Sully 118
  at Vaudricourt 99
  at Vitré La Haye 171
  at Voormezele 50
  Limber Freya 99
  Pole Freya *8*, 15, 50, 56, 99, 122, 135, 168
Frost, Maj. (later Maj.-Gen.) John awarded MC *29*
  and Bruneval Raid 27, *29–30*, 32–34, *42–43*
  commands 'Hardy' section 28
Fruges aircraft reporting station *see* Prédefin

Garrard, Derrick *29*
GEMA, and radar development 12
George VI, King *127*
Germany, post-war British zone 23
Gillard, Frank (BBC) *133*
Göring, Reichsmarschall Hermann and Battle of Britain 10
  personal train 'Robinson' *10*
Goschen, Lt-Col John 13, *27*
Gournay-en-Bray 118
Gravelines
  nuclear power station *56*, *58*
  see also Le Clipon; Petit-Fort-Philippe
Grieve, Sgt David, MM *29*
Ground Control radar sites *18–19*
  Épinay-sur-Duclair 117
  Falaise, Ri *166*, 173
  Le Parc 139
  Le Theil-Nolent 122

Ground Control, Radar Sites — cont.
  Loudéac *166*, 168
  Montcontour *166*
  Monterfil *166*, *170*
  Montrelet 96
  Oisseau, Marêtre *166*, *170*, *172*
  Onglevert 75
  Sully 118
  Vitré La Haye *166*, *170*, 171
  Voormezele 50
Guernsey
  Batterie Mirus *161*
  Clarence Battery *159*
  Fort George, St Peter Port (Target No. 51) 17, *48*, *158–159*
  La Frie Baton *161*
  Pleinemont (Target No. 52) 17, *48*, *160–161*

Hardelot, Boulogne (Target No. 16) 17, *48*, *64*, *83*
Haute Escalles, Pas-de-Calais *180*
Heim, Genlt Ferdinand *79*
Hemmings & Partners *6*
Heston *6*
Hill, F/Lt (later S/Ldr) Antony 25–26, *45*
Hindenburg bunker *see* Douvres-la-Délivrande
Hitler, Adolf 23, *79*
'Hoarding' radar *8*, *11*, 15, 17, 20, 47
  Bellevue, Cap Gris-Nez *70*
  Cap d'Alprech *82*
  Cap d'Antifer *112*
  Cap Fréhel 164
  Caude-Côte 101, *103*
  Chapelle de la Vierge *108*
  Jobourg *155*
  Omonville-la-Rogue 148
  Pointe du Riden 68, 69
  Prédefin *88*, 89
  see also Mammut (Mammoth)
Holden, Kenneth *43*
Hortop, Maj. Al *45*
Houlgate, Sémaphore (Target No. 38) 17, *48*, *126–127*

IFF (Identification Friend or Foe radar) *6*
  FUGe25 German IFF 6, 10
  with Würzburg *12*
Isigny 135
Isle of Wight 27

Jagdschloss radar (Hunting Castle) 22–23
James, Adm. Sir William (C-in-C Portsmouth) 28
Janssen, Gén. Louis *53*
Jersey, Rouge Nez (Target No. 53) 17, *48*, 162
Jobourg, Cap de la Hague (code-name Ammer - Target No. 49) 16, 17, 22, *48*, *127*, *155*
Jones, Dr (later Prof.) Reginald (R. V. Jones)
  Auderville radar station *150*
  and Bruneval radar 24–25, 26, 27, 29–31, 37
  and coastal radar stations 46, *166*
  deception operations *109*

Joubert de la Ferté, AM Sir Philip *150*
Jumel 112

Kafferbitz, Funker Paul *34*
Keil, Oberstlt (Luft-Nachrichten-Regt 53) 22
Kesselring, FM Albert *10*
Knickebein radar *84*

La Belle Étoile *70*
La Brasserie *see* Fermanville
La Chalière, Bernay (Target No. 37) 17, *48*, *124–125*
La Haye *see* Vitré La Haye
La Motte 168
La Poterie 35, 36
La Récompense *see* Loudéac
La Ville la Bas 162
Lanmeur radar station *16*
Laval *171*
Le Clipon
  Loon Plage Motorcross Circuit *56*
  radar station, Gravelines (Target No. 3) 17, *48*, *56–57*, 59
Le Creusot 45
Le Havre 27, *33*, *110*, 112
  see also Bruneval Raid; Cap de la Hève
Le Mesnil, Bayeux (Target No. 64) *48*, *166*, *176–177*
Le Parc, Vire (German code-name Känguruh - Target No. 43) 17, *48*, *139*
Le Theil-Nolent, Lisieux (Target No. 36) 17, *48*, *122–124*
Le Touquet *see* Plage Ste Cécile
Le Tréport *see* Mont Huon
Le Vicel, Barfleur (Target No. 44) 17, *48*, *140–143*
Leffrinckoucke commune *55*
Les Épinais *see* Monterfil
Lindemann Batterie *see* Sangatte
Lisieux *see* Le Theil-Nolent
Lörzer, Gen. Bruno *10*
Loudéac, La Récompense (German code-name Lachs - Target No. 57) 17, *48*, *166*, *168–169*
Louvigné-de-Bais 171

McCallum, L/Cpl John *33*
McIntyre, Rifleman Hugh 32
MacKenzie, Sgt Gregor, MM *29*
McMillan, Richard (United Press) 184
Maimbiers 171
Mammut (Mammoth) radar *11*, 15, *82*
  see also 'Hoarding'
Manifould, F/O Bill *150*
Manneville-ès-Plains *see* St Valéry-en-Caux
Manus, Maj. 47
Marêtre *see* Oisseau
Marlborough 78
Mayenne *172*
Medhurst, AVM Charles 46, 47
Medmenham (Central Interpretation Unit — CIU) *6–8*
  Danesfield House *6–7*
  as Allied Central Interpretation Unit (ACIU) 7
  as Joint Air Photographic Intelligence Centre 7
  as No. 90 Group (Signals) 7
  Auderville *150*

The end of a Würzburg Riese. Unfortunately, the location is not stated.

Medmenham — CIU — continued
  Bruneval radar 25, *26*
  Cap d'Antifer *110, 112–115*
  Target lists *14–16, 36*, 46, 47,
    58–59, 68, 80, 86, 89, 90, 96, 146,
    166, 171, 175, 182
Memorials
  Boulogne (Napoléon I) *78*
  Bruneval Raid 32, *42–45*
  Cap Blanc-Nez (Dover Patrol)
    60, 61, 65
  Douvres-la-Délivrande *132*
  Dover (Zeebrugge action) *60*
  Runnymede Memorial to the
    Missing *115*
Meseke, Obergefr. Wilhelm *34*
MI6 (Secret Intelligence Service)
  46
Mont Boursin 76
Mont Couple wireless station,
  Boulogne 21
Mont de la Louve 75
Mont Huon, Le Tréport (Target
  No. 26) 17, *48, 100*
Mont Lambert, Boulogne (Target
  No. 14) 17, *48, 64, 79*
Mont Plouvin *70*
Mont St Frieux, Neufchâtel
  radar station (Target No. 18) 17,
    48, 85
Mont St Michel 163
Mont Violette (Target No. 17) 17,
  48, 84

Montcontour, Bel-Air (Target No.
  56) 17, *48, 166–167*
Monterfil, Les Épinais (German
  code-name Mandrill - Target
  No. 58) 17, *48, 166, 170*
Montrelet, Amiens (Target No. 24)
  17, *48, 96–97*
Monument, Boulogne (German
  code-name Krokus - Target
  No. 13) 17, *48, 64, 78*
Mountbatten, Adm. Lord Louis
  (later Earl Mountbatten of Burma)
  27, *43*
Museums
  Douvres-la-Délivrande radar
    museum 23, *132, 182–184*
  Pourville, Musée Militaire de
    Dieppe *103*

Napoléon, Emperor, Boulogne
  monument *78*
Naumoff, Lt Peter (commands
  'Drake') 28, 33
Neufchâtel 84
  see also Mont St Frieux; Sully
Neufinck, Col André (code-name
  'Pol') 27
Niblett, S/Ldr John *103*
Nissenthal, F/Sgt Jack, radar station
  raid 13–14, 47, *103*
Noires Mottes, Sangatte 178, *180,*
  181
Norman, G/Capt. Sir Nigel 27, *29*

Nouveau Brighton, Cayeux (Target
  No. 23) 17, *48, 94–95*

Oboe target marking (RAF) 21
Observatoire de Paris 23, *132*
Oisseau, Marêtre (Target No. 60)
  17, *48, 166, 172*
Omonville-la-Rogue (Target No.
  47) 17, *48, 148–149*
Ondrejov Observatory 23
Onglevert, Cap Gris-Nez (Target
  No. 11) 17, *48, 64, 74–75*
Operation
  'Biting' 26, 27, 28, 45
  'Neptune' 17, *18–19*
  'Overlord'
    Arromanches assault *134*
    attacks on radar 15, 16, 20, *21*,
      22, 47, *93, 112, 126, 132,*
      161, 173
    Canadian success *131*
    deception operations *109*
    Juno landing beach *128*
    Pointe du Hoc assault *137*
    threats from radar *166*
  'Taxable' 22, *109*
Orbec 124
Ostend, radar station 47

Paich, Bernard *152, 182*
Paris, Observatoire de Paris 23, *132*
Pas-de-Calais *182*
  coastal batteries *180–181*

Pas-de-Calais — continued
  Göring visits *10*
  radar sites 15, 22
  see also Sangatte
Petit-Fort-Philippe, Gravelines
  (German code-name Krimhild
  - Target No. 4) 17, *48,*
  58–59
Pickard, W/Cdr Charles 27
Plage Ste Cécile (German code-name
  Bulldogge - Target No. 19) 17, *48,*
  86–87
Pleinemont, Guernsey *see*
  Guernsey
Plouguenast 168
Pointe Camberin 68
Pointe d'Ailly 174
Pointe de Jardeheu 148
Pointe du Grouin *see* St Malo
Pointe du Hoc *137*
Pointe du Riden, Cap Gris-Nez
  (German code-name Frundsberg
  - Target No. 8) 17, *48, 64,*
  68–69
Pointe et Raz de la Percée (Target
  No. 41) *14,* 17, 21, *48, 135–137*
Port-en-Bessin *177*
Pourville 47, *101*
Prédefin, Fruges (Target No. 20)
  17, 20, *48, 88–89*
Preussen, Hptm. Hubertus Prinz von
  33
Priest, Don H. (TRE) 34, 47

Quettehou 141

Rennes *171*
Resistance, French 45, 55
  Bruneval raid 27
  and radar sites 15, 20
Reynolds, Quentin 47
'Rhubarb' operations *46,* 47, *48–49,*
  109, 161
Ri *see* Falaise
Ringsted, Germany 23
Roberts, F/O Alfred *127*
Rommel, FM Erwin *154*
Ronce, Belgium *10*
Rosemart 23
Rosendaël 55
Ross, Capt. John 28, 32
Rouge Nez *see* Jersey
Rowe, A. P. 'Jimmy' 46
Ryle, Sir Martin 23

St Aubin-sur-Mer 128
St-Fraimbault 172
Saint-Jouin-Bruneval *see* Bruneval
  Raid
St Léger *see* St Valéry-en-Caux
Saint-Lô *see* Bourg d'Enfer
St Malo, Pointe du Grouin (Target
  No. 54) 17, *48, 163*
Ste Marguerite, Dieppe (Target
  No. 62) *48, 166, 174*
St Martin-aux-Buneaux *see* St
  Valéry-en-Caux
St Péran 170
St Peter Port *see* Guernsey
St Pol, Cap Blanc-Nez (German
  code-name Peilstand 3 - Target
  No. 6) 17, *48, 64, 65*

St Vaast 141
St Valéry-en-Caux
  Manneville-ès-Plains (German
  code-name Fliege - Target
  No. 28) 17, 20, *48, 104–105*
  St Léger (Target No. 63) *48, 166,*
  175
  St Martin-aux-Buneaux (German
  code-name Dora - Target
  No. 29) 17, 20, *48, 106–107*
Sangatte, Calais
  Batterie Lindemann *10,* 22,
  178–181
  radar station (Target No. 65) *48,*
  166, 178–179
Saunders, Andy *40*
Savage, Sgt and Hindenburg
  bunker *182–183, 185*
Saville, F/Lt John *159*
Scarlett, S/Ldr the Hon. Felix *127*
Schlieben, Genlt Karl-Wilhelm von
  154
Scott, Pte Alan *33*
Seine, River *109,* 117
Semaphore stations
  Cap d'Alprech 80
  Cap d'Antifer *110–111*
  Cap de Carteret *156–157*
  Cap de la Hève 121
  Cap Fréhel 17, *48, 164–165*
  Cap Lévy 145
  Houlgate 17, *48, 126–127*
  Le Mesnil, Bayeux 177
  Mont Huon 100
  New Brighton 94
  Pointe de Jardeheu 148
  Pointe et Raz de la Percée 135, 136
  St Malo 163
  Ste Marguerite, Dieppe 174
Senge, Obergefr. Johannes *34*
Serqueux 118
Ships
  British
    Delight (destroyer) *150*
    MGB 317 43
    Prince Albert (landing ship) 29
    Scylla (cruiser) *134*
  United States, *Satterlee*
    (destroyer) *137*
Siegen 23
Siemens radar *128*
Skagen, Denmark 46
SOE (Special Operations Executive),
  and radar site intelligence 15
Somme, River *99*
Songeons 118
Sortosville radar station *16*
Stanmore, German Air Force
  Equipment Centre 23
Stegmann, Genmaj. Rudolf *156*
Strachan, CSM Gerald 32
Stuttgart 23
Sully, Neufchâtel (code-name Biene
  - Target No. 34) 17, *48,*
  118–119
Swanage, Telecommunications
  Research Establishment
  (TRE) *37*
Sweeting, S/Ldr Denis 20

Tait, AVM Victor (Dir. Gen. of
  Signals) 46, 47, *126*

Tardinghen 70, 72
Tedder, AM Sir Arthur 46, 47
Telecommunications Research
  Establishment (TRE) 29, 34, *37,*
  39, 41, 46
Telefunken, and radar development
  12, 21, *41*
Terlincthun 78
Terpe, Oberstlt Emil *34*
The Hague, Netherlands *10*
Theuville 112
Thomas, Pte Daniel *33*
Timothy, Lt John (commands
  'Rodney') 28
Todt Organisation, radar site
  construction 14
Torcé 171
Tragino, River, aqueduct 27

Units, Allied
  Supreme HQ Allied Expedi-
    tionary Force (SHAEF) 47, *126*
  Allied Central Interpretation
    Unit *see* Medmenham
  Allied Expeditionary Air Force
    (AEAF) 21, 46, 47
Units, British
  Combined Operations 27, *43*
  Divisions
    3rd Infantry *131*
    79th Armoured *130–131, 180*
    1st Airborne 27
  Brigades, 44 Parachute *43*
  Regiments
    1st Lothians and Border
      Yeomanry *181*
    22nd Dragoons *131*
    Lincolnshire Regt, 7th Bn *183*
    Parachute *42*
    2nd Parachute Bn *31*
    'C' Coy *26–27, 45*
  Commandos
    No. 30 Assault Unit *134*
    No. 41 (Royal Marine) *130*
  Royal Artillery (RA)
    102nd Light Anti-Aircraft Regt *183*
    147th Field Regt *134*
  Royal Engineers (RE)
    5th Assault Regt *131*
    No. 26 Assault Sqn *131*
    No. 77 Assault Sqn *131*
  RAF Second Tactical Air Force
    20, *47, 103, 109*
  RAF Commands
    Bomber 12, *16,* 21, *181*
    Coastal *109, 150*
    Fighter (later Air Defence of
      Great Britain) 12, 46, *47*
  RAF Groups
    No. 83 Group 20
    No. 84 Group 20
    No. 90 Group (Signals) 7
  RAF Wings, No. 38 (later No. 38
    Group) 27
  RAF Squadrons
    No. 51 (RAF) 27, 28
    No. 158 (RAF) *155*
    No. 164 (RAF) *127*
    No. 174 (RAF) 22
    No. 175 (RAF) 22
    No. 183 (RAF) *127*
    No. 198 (RAF) 20, 47, *103, 127*

RAF Squadrons — continued
    No. 245 (RAF) 22
    No. 439 (RAF) *159*
    No. 441 (RCAF) 21, *112*
    No. 442 (RCAF) 21, *112*
    No. 443 (RCAF) 21, *112*
    No. 543 (RAF) *45*
    No. 609 (RAF) 20, *103, 115*
    No. 617 (RAF) 22, *109*
RAF Units
    Central Interpretation Unit
       (CIU) *see* Medmenham
    No. 1 Photo-Reconnaissance
       Unit 25
    No. 3 Photo-Reconnaissance
       Unit *6*
    RAF Ringway Central Landing
       Establishment 27
    RAF Staff College 46
Royal Navy, Dover Patrol 60, 65
Units, Canadian
    Corps, II *180*
    Divisions, 3rd Infantry *130, 131, 180*
    Brigades
       7th Infantry *180*
       8th Infantry *181*
    Regiments
       6th Armoured (1st Hussars) *180*
       7th Reconnaissance *181*
       10th Armoured (Fort Garry
         Horse) *180*
       Canadian Scottish, 1st Bn
         180
       Highland Light Infantry of
         Canada 67
       North Nova Scotia Highlanders
         79
       Regina Rifles *180*
       Royal Winnipeg Rifles *180*
       South Saskatchewan *103*
    Royal Canadian Artillery (RCA)
       3rd Medium Regt *180*
       12th Field Regt *180*
Units, French, 12ème Div. d'Infan-
    terie Motorisée *53*
Units, German
    Heeresgruppe B *154*
    Divisions
       12. SS-Panzer *131*
       21. Panzer *131*
       77. Infanterie *156*
    Regiments
       Infanterie-Regt 685 33, 35
       Heeres-Küsten-Artillerie-Regt
         1262 *153*
    Batteries
       'Grosser Kurfürst', Framezelle 67
       see also Sangatte
    Kriegsmarine
       2. Marine-Funk-Mess-Abt. 58
       Marine-Artillerie-Abt 204 56
    Luftwaffe
       II. Fliegerkorps *10*
       Regiments
         Luft-Nachrichten-Regt 12 *146*
         Luft-Nachrichten-Regt 23 *101*
         Luft-Nachrichten-Regt 52
           15. Flugmelde-Leit-Komp. *101*
         Luft-Nachrichten-Regt 53
           22, *117–118, 155*
           4. Flugmelde-Leit-Komp *104*
           7. Flugmelde-Leit-Komp. *124*

Units, German, Luftwaffe — continued
           9. Flugmelde-Leit-Komp. *135*
           12. Flugmelde-Leit-Komp. *146*
           13. Flugmelde-Leit-Komp. *155*
           17. Flugmelde-Leit-Komp. *118*
           20. Flugmelde-Leit-Komp. *117*
       Luft-Nachrichten-Regt 54
         7. Flugmelde-Leit-Komp.
         168
       Luftgau-Nachrichten-Regt
         Belgien-Nordfrankreich *101*
       Luftgau-Nachrichten-Regt
         Westfrankreich 25
Units, United States
    Divisions
       9th Infantry *154*
       29th Infantry *135, 136*
    Regiments
       47th Infantry *156*
       60th Infantry *154, 156*
       116th Infantry *135*
    Battalions
       60th Field Artillery *156*
       2nd Ranger *135–137*
    4th Cavalry Group *154*
    USAAF
       Eighth Air Force 20
       Ninth Air Force 20, 21, *47*
       VIII Fighter Command *47*

V-weapons campaign 16, *46, 95*
Vallely, P/O Edward *127, 155*
Vassy *139*
Vaudricourt, Abbeville (German
    code-name Skorpion - Target
    No. 25) 17, *48*, 98–99
Verlincthun 84
Vernon, Lt Dennis, RE 28, 29,
    31
Veule-les-Roses 104
Veulettes 106
Victoria Cross
    not awarded *127*
    and Zeebrugge operation (1918)
    60
Viessoix *139*
Villiers-Fossard *138*
Vire *see* Le Parc
Vitré La Haye (Target No. 59) 17,
    48, 166, 171
Voormezeele, Ypres (Target No. 1)
    17, *48, 50–51, 59*

Walton, Adrian *7*
Waringzelle 69
Warlincthun *70, 75*
Wassermann radar 11, *47, 78, 99,*
    114, 128, 147 see also 'Chimney'
    radar
Wattermel St George, Cap Gris-
    Nez (Target No. 10) 17, *48*, 64,
    72–73
Wavell, S/Ldr Claude 25, 46, *150*
Webb, Sir Aston *60*
Weel, Lenco van der *115*
Wembley, aerial photography
    company *6*
Wenzel, U/off. Gerhard *34*
Wilhelmshaven *183*
Willoughby, Pte John *33*
'Window' anti-radar counter-
    measure 22, *46, 109*

Wissant 70
Wood, F/Lt Robert *115*
Wünsdorf 23
Würzburg radar 8, 17, *110*
    A to D versions *12*
    at Bruneval 25, 27–28, *29, 31–32,*
       33–36, 37, 38, 40, 41
    at Hardelot 83
    at Plage Ste Cécile *86*
    at Pointe du Grouin, St Malo *163*
    at Pointe du Riden 68, 69
    at St Pol 65
    development *12–13*
    Giant (Riese) 8, *13, 22, 23*
       at Arromanches 21, 22, *134*
       at Auderville 150
       at Cap Blanc-Nez *60*
       at Cap d'Alprech 80, *81*
       at Cap d'Antifer 110, *112*
       at Cap de la Hève *15*
       at Cap Fréhel 164
       at Cap Gris-Nez 67
       at Cap Lévy 145
       at Caude-Côte 101, *103*
       at Chapelle de la Vierge *108*
       at Douvres-la-Délivrande *128, 132*
       at Épinay-sur-Duclair *117*
       at Falaise, Ri *173*
       at Fermanville *147*
       at Fort des Dunes 52, *55*
       at Fort George, Guernsey *159*
       at Houlgate, Semaphore *126*
       at Jobourg *155*
       at La Frie Baton, Guernsey *161*
       at Le Clipon *56*
       at Le Parc *139*
       at Le Theil-Nolent *122*
       at Le Vicel *141*
       at Les Épinais, Monterfil *170*
       at Loudéac *168*
       at Manneville-ès-Plains *104, 105*
       at Mont Huon *100*
       at Mont St Frieux *85*
       at Montrelet *96, 97*
       at Nouveau Brighton *94, 95*
       at Oisseau, Marêtre *172*
       at Onglevert 75
       at Petit-Fort-Philippe *59*
       at Pointe et Raz de la Percée
         21, *135, 136*
       at Prédefin *88, 89*
       at St Léger *175*
       at Ste Marguerite, Dieppe *174*
       at Sangatte 22, *178*
       at Sully *118*
       at Vaudricourt *99*
       at Vitré La Haye *171*
       at Voormezele *50*
       at Wattermel St George *72*
    'Michael' anti-jamming device 20
    see also IFF

Y-Bodenstelle *see* 'Benito' radar
Young, Lt Peter (commands
    'Jellicoe') 28, 31
Ypres *see* Voormezele
Yvetot *see* Épinay-sur-Duclair

Zeebrugge operation (1918) *60*
Zerstörer-Säule FuMO 3 Coast-
    watcher aerial *156*
Zuydcoote Battery 52, *53, 55*